Train Technology
For the Tunnel

Conference Planning Panel

G Dallaway, *BSc, CEng, MIMechE* **(Chairman)**
London Underground Limited
London

P R Abrey, *BSc, CEng, FIMechE*
Channel Tunnel High Speed Train
International Project Group
Paris
France

M J Callis, *CEng, FIMechE*
Brush Traction Limited
Loughborough
Leicestershire

M W J Etwell, *BSc, MSc, CEng, FIMechE*
European Passenger Services
British Rail
Derby

N Green, *BSc, CEng, MIMechE*
Consultant
Leicester

M A C Cowan, *BSc, CEng, FIMechE, ACGI, MCIBS*
Eurotunnel
Sutton
Surrey

Proceedings of the Institution of Mechanical Engineers

I MECH E

Train Technology
For the Tunnel

International Conference

4–5 November 1992
Grand Hotel, Le Touquet, France

Sponsored by
Railway Division of the
Institution of Mechanical Engineers

In association with
Institution of Electrical Engineers
Société des Ingenieures et Scientifiques de France
Verband Deutscher Verkehrsunternehmen

IMechE 1992–8

 Published for IMechE by
Mechanical Engineering Publications Limited

ISBN 0 85298 802 8

A CIP catalogue record for this book is available from the British Library.

Printed by Waveney Print Services Ltd, Beccles, Suffolk

Contents

Bus and Train Technology for the '90s

BUS '92

The Expanding Role of Buses Towards the Twenty-First Century

The bus is still the most widely used form of public transport in the world. The contribution of an efficient public transport system in controlling road congestion and reducing environmental pollution is considerable.

This IMechE conference on **Bus '92** brought together experts from all over the world to share their knowledge of bus design and operation.

Thirty five papers were presented on a wide range of topics including design for safety, low emissions through alternative fuels, ways of increasing passenger comfort, electronic developments, and the different urban transport systems in Europe, Hong Kong and Australia.

0 85298 795 1/297x210mm/softcover/290 pages/March 1992 **£88.00**

TRANSIT 2020: Planning, Financing, Design and Operation of Railways Worldwide

Held in London, the birthplace of the Tube, *'Transit 2020'*, records the proceedings of a conference organised by the IMechE to mark the centenary of the world's first deep level railway. Aimed at planners, designers, engineers and operators who are involved in railguided transit, this volume contains the 29 papers presented at the conference.

Contents include:

Central London rail study: Congestion, cure or prevention, Singapore Mass Rapid Transit - the steel way ahead, Human factors in rail passenger transport, Fitting railways for passengers, Potential for railway progress - or product development, technology and resource management, Transit technology assessment.

0 85298 725 0/297x210mm/softcover/216 pages/November 1990 **£87.00**

All prices include **free** delivery within the UK. Overseas customers please add 10%.

Telephone orders using VISA/Mastercard welcome. Please ring 0284 763277 ext. 444

Orders and enquiries:
**Sales Department, Mechanical Engineering Publications Limited,
Northgate Avenue, Bury St Edmunds, Suffolk IP32 6BW, England.
Telephone: 0284 763277   Telex: 817376 Fax: 0284 704006**

Aerodynamic aspects of train design for operation through the Channel Tunnel

R G GAWTHORPE, BSc, MSc, CEng, MIMechE, MRAeS and C W POPE, MSc, PhD
British Rail Research, Derby

SYNOPSIS Rarely have the aerodynamic features of train operations through tunnels shown themselves to be quite so diverse and complex as in the engineering planning for Channel Tunnel services. This Paper illustrates the range of problems affecting train design and operation that have been addressed by making reference to three areas of special importance. These are:

i) The impact of the air flows to and from the Pressure Relief Ducts (PRDs) on the shuttle train and on flexible-sided freight vehicles.

ii) Pressure effects created by the movement of trains in the Tunnel, and how these affect passenger comfort. A description of subjective tests with volunteers in a transient pressure test chamber simulating journeys through the Tunnel is presented.

iii) Determination of the Tunnel wall and rail vehicle aerodynamic roughnesses are described. Their evaluation is extremely important for undertaking predictions of train performance, vehicle pressure loading and the thermal environment.

NOTATION

A_F	frontal area of protuberance
A_D	drag coefficient
C_f	skin friction drag coefficient
D	drag
D_f	form drag
D_S	skin friction drag of longitudinal elements
f_{tu}	friction factor for tunnel (Section 3)
h	total pressure (Δh denotes the loss in total pressure)
L	pressure loss coefficient
R_l	Reynolds number based on length
S_k	Surface area of longitudinal elements
S_{tu}	Surface area of tunnel lining
U	local flow velocity
U_M	mean flow velocity in tunnel
U_m	mean flow velocity over element
V	flow velocity in annulus
ρ	air density

1.   Introduction

This Paper describes by way of example three aspects of research that were undertaken by BR Research to assess the aerodynamic consequences of train operation in the Tunnel.

The basic configuration of the Channel Tunnel consists of two single-track Running Tunnels connected at 250 m intervals with cross-connecting tubes called Pressure Relief Ducts (PRDs). There is also a central Service Tunnel but this does not feature in the main airflow movement caused by train operation. The pressure build-up ahead of a train running through a tunnel and the corresponding pressure deficit behind it (together colloquially called "the Piston Effect") is largely responsible for the aerodynamic drag (and also heat generation) of train operation. The consequent action of the PRD is to reduce these effects by allowing air at positive pressure ahead of a train to bleed across to the other Running Tunnel and similarly allow air to flow back to the negative region behind the train, thus causing a recirculating cell of air to move along with each train (see Fig. 1). At times of trains passing each other in the adjacent Running Tunnels, these cells temporarily interact and cause reinforced or reduced flows.

Although the concept of the PRD results in considerable traction energy savings, lower pressure levels and reduced cooling loads, it also causes certain adverse effects for which due allowance needs to be made. One of the adverse effects that arises from the strong PRD cross flows is that they impinge strongly on the sides of the rear sections of the passing train, and Section 2 describes two tests that were undertaken, one at full-scale and the other at model-scale, to assess the consequences of the PRD flows on shuttle train and network freight train operations.

Section 3 describes laboratory tests undertaken under Contract with volunteer subjects in a pressure chamber at Derby that can faithfully reproduce the pressure histories that either have been predicted to occur or which have been measured for the transit of a train through a tunnel. Such tests were conducted using predicted pressures on a train passing through the

Channel Tunnel in order to ascertain that conditions would be acceptable in terms of passenger comfort for future operations.

The general performance characteristics of a train in a tunnel with regard to aerodynamic drag, the corresponding traction energy consumption and heat output to the tunnel depend strongly not only on the roughness (or frictional air resistance) of the train exterior but also on the roughness of the tunnel walls. Thus, planning of future operations requires an early estimate of the tunnel friction factor from the individual contributions which have to be estimated from track, overhead electric line, tunnel walls and the associated equipment mounted on it. Section 4 of the Paper describes a theoretical appraisal undertaken for Trans Manche Link of the contributions to total friction factor from the components installed in the Channel Tunnel, and an experimental study to obtain friction factors and pressure loss coefficients for the Shuttle trains.

2. CROSS-FLOWS FROM THE PRESSURE RELIEF DUCTS

2.1 Full-Scale Tests of Freight Train Flow Impingement using a Jet Engine

During Channel Tunnel operation, airflows pass through the Pressure Relief Ducts from one Running Tunnel to another. At certain times, the exhaust flows, which can be substantial, impinge on the side of passing trains. Concern was expressed by the network railways about the adverse effects that this could have on certain types of less robust freight wagon, for example, curtain-sided and other types of SWAP body containers. In order to assess the consequences of such flows on the design integrity of these structures, a train consisting of a selection of these wagons and containers was subjected to a simulation of the PRD exhaust flow by running the train through the efflux of a jet engine. The test, which was carried out in the open air, was intended only to simulate the effect of the direct impingement of the PRD flow.

The tests using a jet engine hired from the Motor Industry Research Association were sponsored by BR Railfreight and SNCF and carried out by the Aerodynamics Unit of British Rail Research. As a consequence of this work, EuroTunnel have changed the design criteria for the Tunnel in order to avoid such problems.

Test Arrangement

The jet engine (Fig 2) exhausted into the intake of an annular ejector duct, 15m long and 2m diameter so as to generate a well-mixed flow of realistic velocity profile. The duct was set horizontally at a height above track to impinge at the same point on the wagon sides as the PRD flow in Channel Tunnel. Though, in the Tunnel, the PRD exhausts with a downward component set at 27° to the horizontal, it was considered by EuroTunnel and the network railways that the predominant effects would be simulated sufficiently well by a horizontal flow.

Information provided by EuroTunnel suggested that a regular severe case that network trains would be subjected to during normal heavy traffic operation would be a 2m diameter flow of 50m/s mean velocity. Due to the temperature difference between the "cold" Tunnel flow and the "hot" jet exhaust, the test had to be run with a jet velocity about 10% greater to give the same momentum flow.

The test train consisted (Fig 3) of a selection of international wagons and containers some of which could be prone to damage from cross-flows. In addition, a BR MK3 laboratory coach was used at the tail of the train to house instrumentation signal conditioning and recording equipment. Instrumentation applied to certain of the wagons included straingauges, pressure and displacement transducers, accelerometers, and video cameras set both within certain wagons and also at the trackside.

The test programme consisted of runs at 3 train speeds (20, 40, 60 mile/h equivalent to 32, 64, 96 km/h respectively) and 3 nominal PRD velocities (equivalent to 25, 35, 50 m/s). In addition, static tests were undertaken with the train drawn up alongside the jet outlet to confirm that certain aspects of the test were safe up to jet velocities well in excess of the nominal 50 m/s condition. They were also able to establish in certain cases the threshold velocity at which significant damage or distortion or displacement took place.

Results

The tests, as they stood, indicated that a number of the less robust containers and freight wagon bodies were at considerable risk from the cumulative effects (fatigue loads) of repeated pulses or even from single passes of the full efflux velocity. Whilst the results are applicable only to the specific wagons tested, there were important implications for similar wagon types, or for identical wagons in less original condition.

The effects on the vehicles and containers were all more sensitive to efflux velocity than train speed. It was therefore felt to be of little consequence that the test train was restricted to 60 mile/h maximum speed.

Two of the soft-topped wagon designs had strain measurements on their supporting structure which indicated that structural fatigue problems would occur if regularly operated under the maximum conditions simulated by the test. In one case, the wooden slats supporting the side wall of a certain type of SWAP body collapsed at jet speeds in excess of 47 m/s.

The car on the upper deck of the open car-carrier was moved laterally at just below the 50 m/s reference case with the loss of the restraining effect of the wheel chocks, one of which became detached from the deck floor. Considerable agitation and rocking of the vehicles on their suspension was observed at all jet speeds.

Loosening of the tension fasteners on the 40 foot curtain-sided container was observed when two passes through the jet were performed consecutively at the nominal maximum PRD flow velocity and 60 mile/h train speed. When a number of adjacent straps were detensioned, running under these same conditions produced considerable damage to the curtain.

As a consequence of these tests, EuroTunnel have taken steps to modify the PRD efflux characteristics so as to reduce the effects on the range of likely wagon types to acceptable proportions.

2.2 Model-Scale Tests of Shuttle Train Pressure Loading using a Moving Model Rig

As already described, the prime function of the pressure relief ducts (PRDs) is to facilitate the movement of air from a high pressure region in one tunnel to a low pressure region in the other. The low pressure regions are often in the vicinity of the rear parts of a moving train, (Fig 1), and, therefore, flow through the PRD will exhaust on to the sides of the rear vehicles. At the leading end of a train, flow passes through the PRD into the adjacent tunnel causing a suction effect on forward vehicles. Calculations show that the flow velocities through the PRDs are of the order of 50 m/s. Tests have been conducted using a 1/20th scale static model at Institut AeroTechnique (IAT), St Cŷr to measure the forces and reduce their magnitude using deflector plates.

It has been felt, however, that the results could be modified by the effect of the trains forward motion. Accordingly, a series of tests have been conducted on BRs Moving Model Test Facility (1) under contract to EuroTunnel to investigate the effect of forward motion past a pressure relief duct. Experiments were conducted with and without a deflector plate in place under static and moving conditions for both the suction and exhaust (blowing) cases. The "static" case was simulated by towing the model train past the PRD at very low speed (1m/s).

The "moving" cases were performed using model speeds of the order of 30m/s.

Testing was conducted using a scale of 1/30.4 with a 20m long model tunnel possessing an accurate roughness simulation 2m fore and aft of a model pressure relief duct. The pressure relief duct was situated 4m from the exit of the tunnel with suction or blowing flows of 50m/s generated through the duct by a fan, (Fig 4). Allowance was made to fit a deflector plate over the mouth of the PRD. This took the form of a gauze and possessed a blockage of 50%.

A 4.12m (equivalent to 140m full-scale) long model was constructed of the shuttle train comprising of a locomotive, loading vehicle and three carrier vehicles. At full scale, the largest side forces for the suction condition are generated when the train is curving and takes up its minimum clearance between the cant rail and the tunnel wall of 450mm on the PRD side of the tunnel. In order to simulate this condition during the suction cases, provision was made to tilt the model superstructure towards the PRD as shown in Fig 5.

Surface static pressures were measured at fourteen locations around the centre of the penultimate vehicle, using miniature strain gauge pressure transducers. The pressures were recorded using an on-board battery powered data logger (Fig 6) and down-loaded for processing by computer at the end of each run.

The speed history of the train and time at which the tapping plane passed the PRD were determined using an infra red sensor.

The pressures were integrated over the vehicle surface to evaluate the side force, the rolling moment and the yawing moment using a specially developed computer program. Within the program, it was assumed that the variation of circumferential pressure with time behaved like that on an infinitely long body (i.e that there were no losses near the inter-vehicle gaps). Knowing the time at which the tapping plane was coincident with PRD, the speed history of the train was then used to transform the pressure distribution giving the variation of pressure with distance from the centre line of the PRD.

In the program simulation, the reference penultimate vehicle passes through the pressure distribution in successive time steps each of which corresponds to a specific distance from the PRD, (Fig 7). At each interval, appropriate integrations of the pressure distributions are carried out to give the force and moment coefficients. In this way, graphs are generated which give the variation of the coefficients for the vehicle as a whole with its distance from the PRD.

The results concluded the following:

(a) For the PRD suction case, both forward motion of the train and the fitting of the deflector plate have little effect on the side force, rolling moment and yawing moment compared to the results with a "static" model and with no deflectors respectively. Indeed the degree of correspondence obtained from the repeat cases is remarkably close.

(b) For the blowing case without the deflector plate fitted, forward motion appears to produce an increase of 35% in the peak side force. There are also increases of 39% and 27% in the peak rolling moment and the positive peak of the yawing moment respectively.

(c) In the case of blowing with a deflector fitted, there is very little effect of forward motion. Relative to the blowing case with forward speed in the absence of a deflector, fitting of a deflector reduces the peak side force by 58%. Further, the rolling and yawing moments are both reduced by about 50%. It is apparent, therefore, that the deflector plate has a very significant effect on reducing the side force, rolling and yawing moments produced by the blowing conditions.

3. COMFORT TESTS IN THE DERBY TRANSIENT PRESSURE TEST CHAMBER

It was important for EuroTunnel and TransManche Link to know at a relatively early stage in the design development of the Channel Tunnel that the air pressure conditions inside shuttle trains operating through the Tunnel would be acceptable to people.

It was realised that the interconnections of the two Running Tunnels via the PRDs would cause a particularly complex pattern of pressure changes to occur as the two groups of varied traffic (Shuttle trains with high speed through trains with low speed freight trains) entered the Tunnel and proceeded to pass each other. Studies already undertaken by BR Research suggested that the pressure changes would not be as abrupt as those found in existing tunnels (because of the attenuation caused by the more devious path taken by the pressure waves between the two sets of traffic) but that the overall changes over a matter of minutes would be unusually high (essentially because of the length of the Tunnel). In addition, small but rapid changes were expected to occur on each train as they passed the open ends of each PRD. Another feature not already met in existing experience was the effect of passing beneath the coastal ventilation shafts.

Included in EuroTunnels specification for the Tunnel based on work undertaken previously by BR were the following two criteria for maximum pressure change:

(a)   a maximum change of 3kN/m^2 within a period of 3 seconds for individual pulses.

(b)   a maximum change of 0.45kN/m^2 for frequently repeating pulses.

Acknowledging the experience gained by BR Research in this field of work (2,3,4) which had involved the development in the early 1970s of a transient pressure test chamber at Derby in which the pressure conditions of complete journeys through, for example, the Channel Tunnel could be simulated, ET/TML let a Contract to BRR to provide a statistically–based judgement with volunteer subjects of the acceptable nature of these conditions. The Institute for Consumer Ergonomics at Loughborough undertook the human factors aspects of the test and analyzed the statistical results.

Briefly, the BRR Pressure Chamber (Fig 8) consists of a sealed box with large window area capable of seating 2 people in comfort. The roof consists of a bellows which can be moved by a hydraulic ram itself actuated by signals derived from pre–recorded magnetic tape or solid state PC memory. The performance of the ram is such that it can faithfully follow the pressure changes and rates of change associated with rail operation in tunnels.

The Channel Tunnel tests consisted of playing into the chamber a predicted pressure history (actually predicted by Mott Macdonald) (see Fig 9) of the conditions existing aboard a EuroTunnel Shuttle train during two notional journeys through the Tunnel. At certain points (ten in all) through the journey, pre–chosen to be times soon after significant pressure events had taken place, the volunteer subjects were asked to respond to the following question:

"How unpleasant, if at all, did you find that section of the journey?"

Not at all unpleasant [| | | | | |] Extremely unpleasant

The subjects responded by ticking the appropriate box on the 7 point scale. At the end, they were asked amongst other things to give an overall rating for the journey as a whole.

Fig 10 illustrates the results of the tests. It shows the results for two different Channel Tunnel journeys (designated A & B) at each of the 10 sections through the journeys together with the "overall" rating at the end. The severity of the response is indicated as a rating 1 through 7 for the box ticked, and the "frequency" indicates the number of people (out of a total sample of 30) marking each box. The median and 90th percentile points are shown. Mean rating values across all 30 subjects were 2.13 and 2.30 for A & B, and standard deviations between all subjects were 1.33 and 0.95 respectively. Journey A was predicted to be a typical journey in busy traffic conditions with a mixture of ET Shuttle trains and BR/SNCF through trains operating in both Running Tunnels. The pressures represented those felt by a passenger positioned near the front of a shuttle train travelling from England to France. The speed profile of the train was that corresponding to a constant traction power output, and a maximum speed of approximately 160 km/h was reached for part of the journey. Though a typical journey, the phasing of the trains passing in the two running tunnels was carefully chosen, in Case A, to produce a superpositioning of severe pressure waves (2.8 kPa in 4s) from the various trains, coinciding with the large pressure variation caused when the train passes beneath the first coastal ventilation shaft.

The second chosen journey (Case B) is a hypothetically worse case than Case A assuming that various adverse contingencies, involving increased train drag, tunnel friction, and hence pressures, materialise and summate to produce a notional worst case giving pressures 25% greater than those of A.

The general results were felt to convey a situation that could not be considered unacceptable. However, they did suggest that the most severe conditions by far occurred during Section 2 of the journeys, where 3 and 5 people respectively out of the total of 30 (10% and 17% for Journey A & B respectively) rated it as "7 – extremely unpleasant". The severe pressures in Section 2 were associated with passing beneath the coastal ventilation shaft and it has been possible to modify the shaft arrangement to reduce substantially this effect. This example illustrates the considerable advantage that such a test can bring by identifying a potential problem in time for a remedy to be conceived and implemented.

4

4.0 DETERMINATION OF THE AERODYNAMIC COEFFICIENTS FOR THE TUNNEL AND SHUTTLE TRAINS

4.1 Tunnel Friction Factor

4.1.1 Nature of roughness

The surface finish of the Channel Tunnel and the fixed equipment located in the tunnel are quite unlike those of any other railway tunnel. As a result it is not possible to use data from existing railway tunnels to obtain an estimate of the friction factor. This has necessitated the development under Contract to TML/Mott Macdonald of a special method for its evaluation.

The tunnel is unique in that it possesses a cooling system. This comprises two pipes which run the length of the tunnel and are supported at regular intervals on fabricated steel brackets. Walkways, hand rails, lights, cables and cable trays will be also be present together with a catenary which is a regular feature of many tunnels. Much of the lining is of smooth concrete: some sections for geological reasons are, however, reinforced with circumferential ribs. Fig 11 shows the tunnel cross section and gives details of the principal roughness elements.

4.1.2 Method of Analysis

In the analysis, the drag of all the roughness features in the tunnel has been estimated and a friction factor obtained from the results. For the purposes of the analysis, the roughnesses are divided into form roughnesses and skin friction elements. The form roughnesses are further divided into isolated and closely spaced protuberances.

(a)   Form Roughness

(i)   isolated protuberances:
overhead wire supports, rods and insulators overhead wire droppers, lights.

(ii)   closely spaced protuberances:
joints between concrete sections, sleepers and spacers, rail clips, cooling system brackets, cooling main flanges, lagging straps, cable tray brackets, hand rail supports.

(b)   Skin friction elements
basic concrete lining, bolted steel lined sections, cooling mains, overhead wires, rails, cable trays, leaky feeders, longitudinal hand rails.

Form Roughness

In estimating the drag, it has been assumed that the velocity profile is a 1/7 power law. This is applied to estimate the average flow velocity over the height of each element.

For the closely spaced protuberances, there is a danger of over estimating the velocities which exist in the neighbourhood of the various elements. These roughnesses are well within the boundary layer and behave so as to influence the flow over the entire cross section. The protuberances have, therefore, been treated as roughnesses which stretch round the periphery of the tunnel and an effective height deduced from their frontal area.

Drag coefficients for the estimation of the drag on individual roughness elements have been obtained from Hoerner (5) for structures of a similar shape and the drag obtained from

$$D \quad = \quad \frac{1}{2} \, \rho \, U^2 \, A_F \, C_D$$

Skin Friction Elements

The skin friction drag coefficient of individual longitudinal elements such as wires, rails, cooling mains, and cable trays is given by a relationship due to Schlichting (6) modified for high Reynolds numbers.

The skin friction coefficient of the tunnel lining is given by the Moody formula.

The skin friction drag of each component is then deduced from

$$D_f \quad = \quad \frac{1}{2} \, \rho U_m^2 \, S_K \, C_f$$

Evaluation of Friction Factor

Using the above approach the total friction factor is obtained from

$$f_{tu} \quad = \quad \frac{\Sigma D}{\frac{1}{2} \rho \, U_M^2 \, S_{tu}}$$

Table 1 shows an early evaluation of the total drag on the tunnel roughness elements for a flow velocity of 10m/s. The total drag corresponds to a friction factor of 0.012. It is shown that major contributions come from the track and cooling system (64%).

On the basis of evaluations like this, it has been decided to refine the design of the cooling main brackets and introduce measures to reduce track system protrusions. These measures will reduce the friction factor by around 25% and result in a useful decrease in the train drag.

Comparison with measurements of the drag of roughness elements in a 1/20th scale model constructed at IAT, St Cŷr have shown the calculation method to give very realistic results.

4.2　Aerodynamic Coefficients for Shuttle Train

At an early stage in the design of the tunnel it was necessary to obtain an indication of the drag of the shuttle trains. The drag is dependent on three coefficients; the nose pressure loss coefficient, train friction factor and tail pressure loss coefficient. As the trains were of a unique design and extrapolations from existing results were likely to be unreliable, it was necessary to obtain the results from a dedicated test at model scale as part of a Contract to TML. A simple approach was used in which 1/85 scale models of shuttle trains were placed in a simulation of a section of the Channel Tunnel, (Fig 12). Known rates of flow were drawn over the models and the coefficients deduced from pressure drop measurements.

Friction factors were obtained for the configurations listed in Table 2. From Table 2 it is seen that inter-car gaps only have a secondary effect on the friction factor. Removal of the underbody fairings increased the friction factor by 44%. It should, however, be borne in mind that removal of the fairings results in a significant reduction of the cross sectional area of the vehicle. If the underbody remains smooth between the bogies then the aerodynamic drag only increases by about 2%.

The loss coefficients were determined for a range of leading and trailing end configurations. These, with the loss coefficients obtained, are shown in Table 3. In the table, a decrease in loss coefficient indicates an improvement in aerodynamic behaviour. The loss coefficient is defined as

$$L = \frac{\Delta h}{\frac{1}{2}\rho V^2}$$

Some of the loss coefficients are negative. This is because the area of the train is based on the area of the carrier vehicles which is much larger than the locomotives and loading vehicles at the ends of the train. Under these circumstances, an artificially reduced coefficient results.

(a)　Loss of leading locomotive & loading vehicle

Where an open loading vehicle is interposed between the locomotive and the leading carrier vehicle radiusing the corner of leading carrier vehicle results in an improved flow around the forward end. This manifests itself as a reduction in the loss coefficient from 0.037 to − 0.16.

Use of a telescopic loader results in a further reduction in the loss coefficient to − 0.33. An additional improvement could be effected by radiusing the leading edges of the loader. A small improvement (Table 3) is afforded by the use of a streamlined nose on the locomotive.

(b)　Loss of trailing loader and locomotive

An open loading vehicle gives a lower loss than a telescopic loader. This is probably due to a system of trailing vortices which are shed from the sloping edges of the telescopic vehicle. As might be expected the configuration with the bluff locomotive gives the largest loss.

(c)　Open central loading vehicles

A pair of open loaders results in a loss of 0.41 dynamic head.

In order to append meaning to the friction factor and pressure loss data, calculations of the total train drag are shown in Table 4 for various configurations of interest. (Single train movements, PRDs closed.)

Similar values of aerodynamic drag result for trains with both open and closed loading vehicles. The front end design of the locomotive does not have a very significant effect on the drag due to the dominant effect of skin friction on the carrier vehicles.

Fairing in the bogies, however, is likely to result in a significant decrease in the drag.

5.　CONCLUSIONS

The paper describes a variety of unusual and difficult aerodynamic problems associated with future Channel Tunnel operations which have been investigated by British Rail Research in a number of novel ways. The results of the work have enabled early decisions to be made, or early information to become available, which have facilitated plans for new or modified train design and have developed confidence in future Tunnel operation.

Acknowledgement

An acknowledgement is made to the British Railways Board, to SNCF, to EuroTunnel and to TransManche Link for permission to publish this paper. Thanks are also due to colleagues of the authors in the Aerodynamics Unit and elsewhere at British Rail Research for their assistance in the work leading to the Paper.

REFERENCES

1.　POPE C W., "The simulation of flows in railway tunnels using a 1/25th scale moving model facility", 7th International Symposium on the Aerodynamics and Ventilation of Vehicle Tunnels, organised by BHRG, Cranfield, held at Brighton, November 1991, pp 709–737.

2. GAWTHORPE R G: "Human tolerance to rail tunnel pressure transients – a laboratory assessment". In: Proc 5th Int. Symp on the Aerodynamics and Ventilation of Vehicle Tunnels (Lille, France, 20–22 May 1985). BHRA Fluid Eng, Cranfield, UK 1985. Paper C4, 18pp.

3. GAWTHORPE, R G: "Predicted passenger response to rail tunnel pressure transients" In: Proc 6th Int Symp on the Aerodynamics and Ventilation of Vehicle Tunnels (Durham, England, 27–29 Sept 1988). BHRA Fluid Engineering, Cranfield, UK. 1988 Paper A3, 16pp.

4. GAWTHORPE, R G: "Pressure Comfort Criteria for Rail Tunnel Operations" In: Proc. 7th Int Symp on the Aerodynamics and Ventilation of Vehicle Tunnels (Brighton, England, 27–29 Sept 1991). Organized by BHR Group, Cranfield, UK.

5. HOERNER, S F. "Fluid Dynamic Drag". Published by the author, 148 Busteed Drive, Midland Park, New Jersey, USA, 1958.

6. SCHLICHTING, H, "Boundary Layer Theory". McGraw Hill, 6th Edition, 1966.

TABLE 1
FRICTION FACTOR AND BREAKDOWN OF FRICTIONAL DRAG FOR CONTINUOUS FLOW VELOCITY OF 10 M/S

FRICTION FACTOR = 0.0117
ROUGHNESS HEIGHT = 0.133m

	ITEM	DRAG kN	TOTAL
TRACK	(a) Rail (b) Sleepers (c) Rail Spacers (d) Rail Clips	2 187 42 14	245 kN
LINING	(e) Wall–Smooth Sections (f) Joints–Raised (g) Joints–Depressed (h) Wall–Bolted Sections	192 5 3 85	285 kN
COOLING SYSTEM	(i) Cooling Mains and associated components (j) Flanges (k) Straps (l) Cooling Main Brackets	32 50 5 282	369 kN
OVERHEAD	(m) Wire Supports (n) Droppers (o) Contact Wire (p) Support Wire	18 3 0 0	21 kN
OTHER	(q) Hand Rail (r) Leaky Feeder (s) Cable Trays (t) Brackets for (v) (u) Lights (v) Miscellaneous	6 1 6 9 11 2	35 kN
		TOTAL	955 kN

TABLE 2

TRAIN FRICTION FACTORS

Configuration	Friction Factor
Idealised model. No bogies. No intercar Gaps.	0.0055
With bogies and intercar gap of 0.43 m (full–Scale)	0.0083
With bogies and 0.43 m gap. No underbody fairings	0.0141

TABLE 3

LOSS COEFFICIENTS FOR TRAIN END GEOMETRIES

	Configuration	Loss Coefficients
Leading end	Streamlined Locomotive and open loading vehicle with sharp edges on leading carrier vehicle	0.037
	Streamlined locomotive open loading vehicle with radiused edges on leading carrier vehicle	−0.16
	Streamlined locomotive and telescopic loading vehicle with sharp leading edges	−0.33
	Bluff nosed locomotive and telescopic loading vehicle with sharp leading edges	−0.24
Trailing end	Streamlined locomotive and open loading vehicle	−0.12
	Streamlined locomotive and telescopic loading vehicle	0.04
	Bluff locomotive and telescopic loading vehicle	0.12

TABLE 4

AERODYNAMIC DRAG PREDICTIONS

	Nose Loss	Tail Loss	Train Friction	Drag Coefficient	Drag N x 10^6
Case 1	−0.33	−0.04	0.0055	20.9	0.39
Case 2	−0.33	−0.04	0.0083	28.4	0.53
Case 3*	−0.33	−0.04	0.0080	27.7	0.52
Case 4*	−0.03	−0.12	0.0080	28.4	0.53
Case 5*	−0.16	−0.12	0.0080	27.7	0.52
Case 6+	−0.24	−0.03	0.0141	34.2	0.54
Case 7	−0.24	−0.12	0.0083	29.9	0.54

*Friction factor reduced in accordance with reduced to pressure losses associated with open loading vehicles.

+Train cross–sectional area and perimeter reduced to allow for removal of underbody fairings. Modified nose and tail losses to be consistent with reduced areas.

Case 1	Ideal case. No bogies or intercar gaps. No loading vehicles.
Case 2	Streamlined locomotive and telescopic loading vehicles. Underbody fairings on carriers, faired central loading vehicles and 0.43 m intercar gaps.
Case 3	As 2 but with open central loading vehicle.
Case 4	Streamlined locomotive and open loading vehicle with square corners on leading end of adjacent carrier vehicle. Underbody fairings on carriers, open central loading vehicles and 0.43 m intercar gaps.
Case 5	Same as Case 4 but leading carrier with rounded corners.
Case 6	Same as Case 2 but with no underbody fairings.
Case 7	Same as Case 2 but with a bluff nosed locomotive.
	(Train speed 140 km/h, PRDs closed, single train movements.)

C451/003

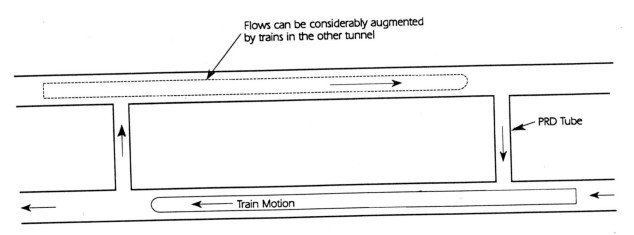

Flows can be considerably augmented by trains in the other tunnel

PRD Tube

Train Motion

Fig. 1 Flow Recirculation induced by PRD s and Vehicle Motion

(Photo: MIRA)

Fig.2 Jet Engine "cross flow generator" and passing train

(Photo: MIRA)

Fig.3 Part of Test Train showing Lab Coach and instrumented containers

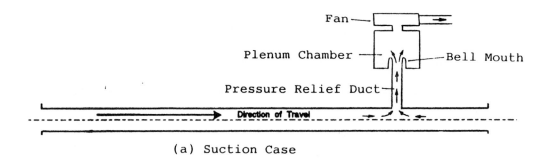

(a) Suction Case

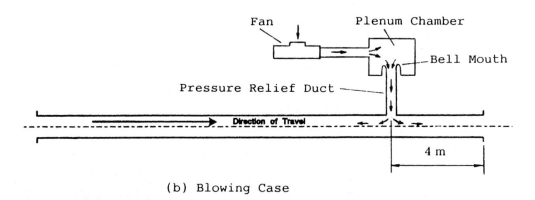

(b) Blowing Case

Fig.4 Moving Model Rig - Simulation of PRD Flows

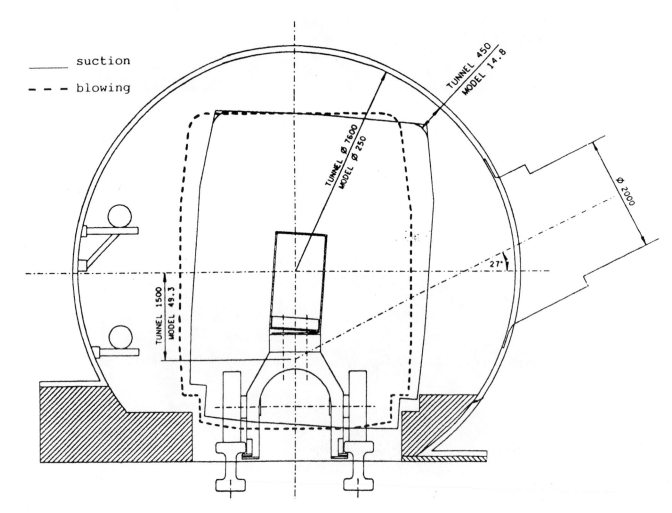

Fig.5 Cross-section showing angle of train model for suction and blowing cases

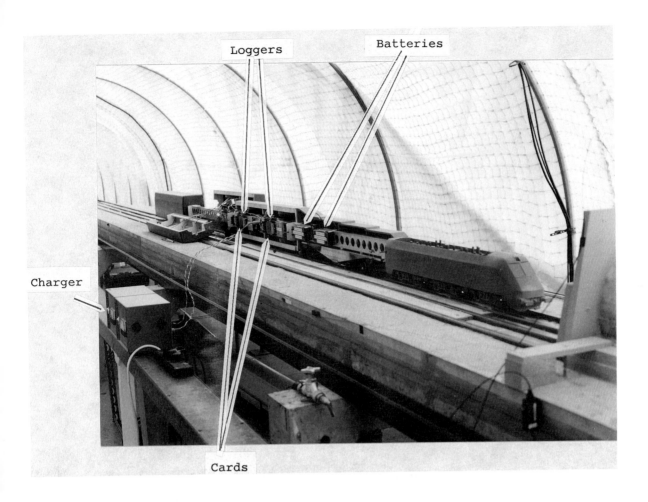

Fig.6 Model Shuttle Train showing internal data logger

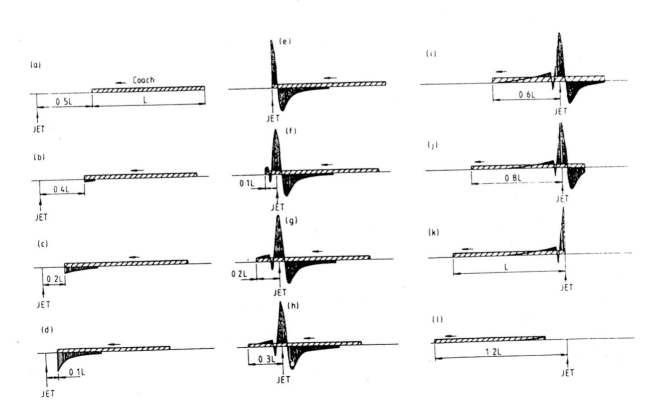

Fig.7 Pressure Distribution over "Swept Area" of reference vehicle when passing PRD

Fig.8 Derby Transient Pressure Test Chamber

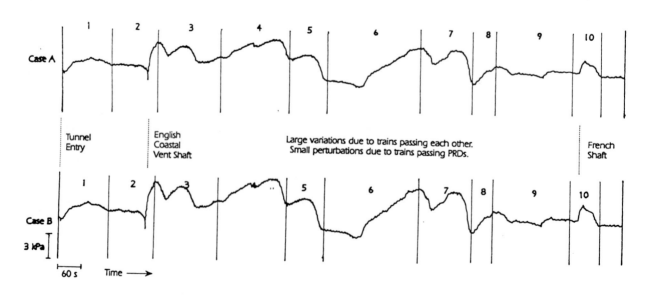

Fig.9 Pressure Histories for Shuttle Train passengers simulated in Pressure Chamber Tests

C451/003

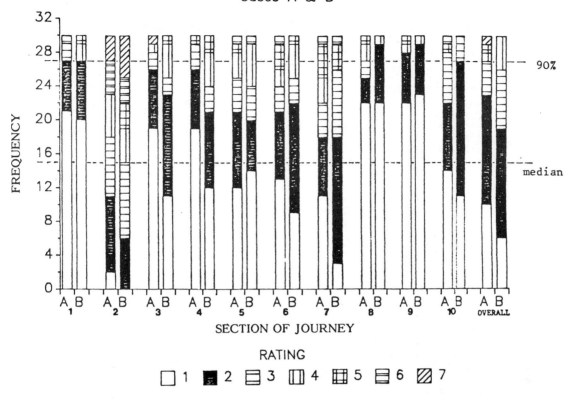

Fig.10 Subjective "Unpleasantness" Rating Distributions for Channel Tunnel "journeys"

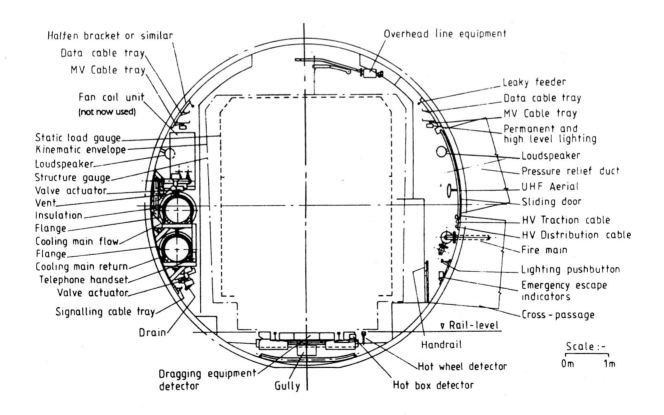

Fig.11 Cross-section showing detail of tunnel fitments.

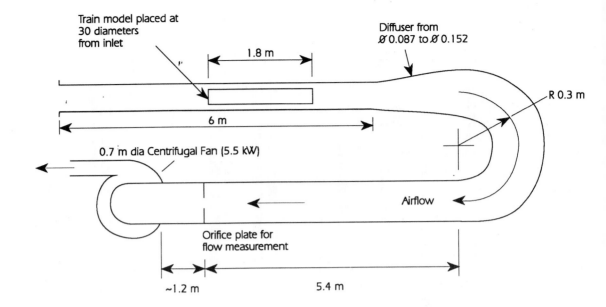

Fig.12 Schematic Diagram of Static Test Rig

© British Railways Board 1992

C451/033

Pressures on rolling stock design

W M S BRADBURY, MA, DIC, PhD, CEng, MIMechE, MRAeS
W S Atkins and Partners, and Eurotunnel, Sutton, Surrey
D A HENSON, BSc, PhD, CEng, MICE
Mott Macdonald, Croydon, Surrey
M E GILL, MA, PhD, CEng, MIMechE
W S Atkins and Partners, Epsom, Surrey

1. SYNOPSIS

Rolling Stock for the Channel Tunnel must be designed to withstand pressures caused by a variety of aerodynamic mechanisms.

This paper describes the types of aerodynamic mechanisms which must be considered and shows how these can be analysed. Illustrative assumptions are stated and corresponding pressure load predictions are presented.

2 INTRODUCTION

The Channel Tunnel is 50 km long. It is in fact three tunnels with multiple aerodynamic interconnections ("piston relief ducts" and railway cross overs between the two running tunnels, "cross passages" from the central service tunnel, and ventilation shafts from the atmosphere).

Rolling Stock conceived for the Channel Tunnel - or for any other long complex rail tunnel - must withstand substantial aerodynamic pressure loads.

These arise from the movement of the train itself, movement of other trains, as well as various local effects (such as coupler compression or Halon release). These pressure loads need to be quantified in order to define the structural loads, and fatigue ratings, for the wagon design specification.

This paper describes how these various pressure loadings can be calculated. For the purposes of this paper the operating circumstances considered have been simplified but the main effects are apparent. Determination of these pressure loadings includes compressible flow network predictions, "leaky box" calculations, and elementary analysis of heat transfer between air and wagon.

Structural pressure loads such as those predicted are input to the structural design process. Loads which are experienced repeatedly are taken into account in the fatigue rating, where the number of cycles in the wagon lifetime is also important.

Note: quantitative assumptions taken for this paper are listed as Appendix 1. These figures should be regarded as indicative. The actual figures taken as a basis for Channel Tunnel Rolling Design now differ for some parameters.

The calculations relate to a twin-deck wagon which would carry passengers and their cars.

3 OPERATING CIRCUMSTANCES

The aerodynamic environment in the tunnel depends on the operating circumstances at the time. The relevant circumstances include the number and types of trains in the tunnel, their speeds and locations, the configuration of crossover doors and piston relief duct dampers, etc.

Clearly there exists a great range of possibilities. Certain representative operating conditions have to be identified to define design conditions. For Rolling Stock design two particular classes are needed: Operating circumstances leading to "extreme loads"; and frequently recurring circumstances which cause "fatigue loads".

The choice of representative operating circumstances is not easy. A judgement has to be made on the basis of understanding of the system, its design and its operation. The "extreme" circumstances chosen should represent conditions which could conceivably happen without postulating an unrealistic coincidence of unlikely rare events. The "fatigue" circumstances chosen must represent a normal type of operation although this may never exactly be achieved in practice.

The representative circumstances chosen as a basis for the Channel Tunnel Rolling Stock design are inevitably complicated. These may involve numbers of shuttles moving, braking or stopping while various tunnel doors or dampers are operating or are in abnormal configurations.

For this paper, rather simpler circumstances have been chosen. Although these are not quite as severe, the principles are the same, and it is easier to explain and understand the physics of the situation.

The various operating circumstances assumed for this paper are listed in Appendix 2. Fatigue loadings result from repetitive events in normal operation, such as tunnel entry effects, self induced pressures as the shuttle passes piston relief ducts and the effects of passing a shuttle in the other tunnel. Extreme loads result from events experienced much less often, for example, tunnel entry at higher than normal speed, or passing a shuttle stopped in the other tunnel.

The pressures and air velocity histories which correspond to these circumstances and which are required for the pressure load calculations are calculated by the compressible flow network program. These pressure and velocity histories are also included as figures 1 to 7.

4 TYPES OF EFFECT

The design must account for various types of pressure effect.

4.1 Rapid Transient Effects

As a shuttle moves through the tunnel, the pressure in the tunnel will increase due to the piston effect of the shuttle. Pressures of 5kPa (or more) above ambient may be experienced. However, during a gradual rise in pressure, the leakage of air into the wagon will equalise the pressure, and hence this will not subject the wagon structure to any significant pressure load. In rapidly changing pressure conditions, where there is not time to equalise the pressure, there will be a significant pressure differential across the structure. The following calculations are concerned with the loadings which result.

Obviously, a very leaky wagon structure would suffer much smaller values of differential pressure, as well as being cheaper to manufacture. However it would not give the passengers sufficient protection from external pressure transients, and it would be less effective at retaining smoke or Halon in the event of a fire. The target level of leakage which has been chosen in the design of the wagons is considered to represent a good compromise.

Pressure transients causing structural loads may be the result of a change in internal or external pressure. Slightly different calculations are needed for each.

4.1.2 External pressure transients

Circumstances causing external transients are: trains entering tunnels, passing shafts or piston relief ducts; interactions between trains; opening or closing of tunnel doors or barriers; and, possibly, local pressure fluctuations in the annulus alongside the train.

4.1.3 Internal pressure transients

Events which could cause internal transients are coupler compression, on-board Halon release and rapid thermal expansion. Each of these results in a structural pressure load until flow through the wagons' leaks allows equilibrium to be regained.

4.2 Longitudinal Pressure Gradients

A train moving through a tunnel induces the air in the tunnel to move with it. The speed of the air ranges from a value approaching the train speed for a close fitting train in a short tunnel, to a very low value for a small train in a very large tunnel. In the steady state the forward impulse of the train, equal to the resistive force on the train, balances the resistance forces of the air in the tunnel. In a very long tunnel such as the Channel Tunnel, the air resistance is very high, so that the resistive force on the train is also high. This appears as a very large pressure difference between the front and rear of the train.

This produces a steep pressure gradient down the length of the train in the annulus space outside the train.

Although the shuttle wagons are quite well sealed, there are doors in the barriers between wagons. When these are open a pair, or group, can become aerodynamically interconnected. For this paper it is assumed that up to 4 internal doors could be open simultaneously, allowing interconnection of 3 wagons.

This situation would produce constant internal pressure along the length of these three wagons. This constant pressure would be close to the external pressure at the middle of the middle wagon.

With constant pressure on the inside, and a gradient of pressure on the outside, a pressure difference occurs across the structure. The greatest difference (and hence greatest structural load) occurs on the ends of the end wagons.

4.3 Local Pressure Relief Ducts Pressure Effects

The movement of the shuttle in the tunnel creates a flow of air in the tunnel and through the piston relief ducts. The air flow through the PRD's, which is directed away from the shuttle at the front and towards the shuttle at the rear, will cause a pressure loading on the body of any shuttle adjacent to the piston relief duct. Repetitive local pressure effects will exist at the rear of a shuttle, due to the impingement of this air jet created by the shuttle's own movement. A shuttle stopped in the tunnel will experience extreme pressure effects due to the PRD air jets created by shuttles moving in the other tunnel.

5 METHOD OF ANALYSIS

The Aerodynamic Environment corresponding to the specified operating circumstances is predicted using the Compressible Flow Network Programme described in Appendix A3.1

Appendix A3.2 describes the adiabatic analysis of airflows through wagon leaks. Appendices A3.3 and A3.4 describe the thermodynamic analysis of on-board Halon release and the thermal expansion which could occur in the event of a fire. Appendix A3.5 describes analysis of the effects of bellows compression.

The basis for estimates of local pressure effects is described in Appendix A3.6

6 RESULTS

The results of the calculation follow as two tables. Table 1 gives predicted extreme differential pressures (Pa). Table 2 gives predicted typical ("fatigue") differential pressures (Pa) together with indicative cycle counts.

7 CONCLUSIONS

The range of operating circumstances and events which can cause aerodynamic pressure loads has been considered. Corresponding predictions have been made.

These predictions suggest that "internal" loading mechanisms (such as coupler compression and Halon release) are as important as "external" loading mechanisms ("piston effect").

The result from calculations such as those described are used to determine the structural specification for the shuttle wagon designs.

Table 1. Extreme Loads (Pa)

Effect	Longitudinal Pressure Gradient	Rapid Transients	PRD Local Pressures	Halon Release	Rapid Thermal Expansion	Bellows Compression
Walls	±265	-1357	-2437	+1863	+1400	0
Barriers	±265	-1357	0	+1948	+1485	±4300
Roof	±265	-1357	0	+1863	+1400	0

Table 2. Fatigue Loads (Pa)

Effect	Portal Entry Normal	Portal Entry Single Line	PRD Pulses	PRD Local Pressures	Shuttles Passing	Annulus Pressure Fluctuations	Incident Wave from Portal Entry	Bellows Compression
Walls	-130	-309	±51	+238 -898	+202	±200	-188	0
Barriers	-130	-309	±51	0	+202	±200	-188	±860
Roof	-130	-309	±51	0 24 x 10^6	+202	±200	-188	0
No of cycles	0.12 x 10^6	12 x 10^3	24 x 10^6		1.2 x 10^6	3.6 x 10^8	10 x 10^3	0.6 x 10^6

Notes: Positive values indicate wagon internal pressure > external pressure.
Calculations are for 0.04m^2 leakage area (time constant 5 seconds).
Wagon life = 30 years x 2000 transits/year.

These figures are indicative only, actual rolling shock design is based on values which may be significantly different.

8 REFERENCES

Henson DA & Fox JA "Transient Flows in Tunnel Complexes of the type proposed for the Channel Tunnel" proceedings of IMechE 188 15/74).

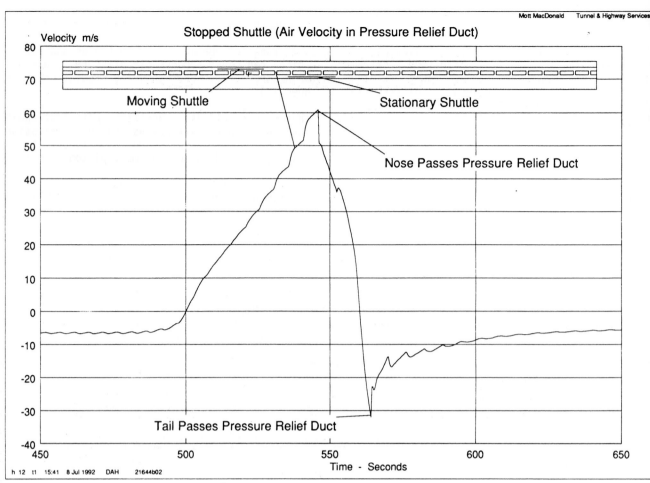

Figure 1   -   Stopped Shuttle

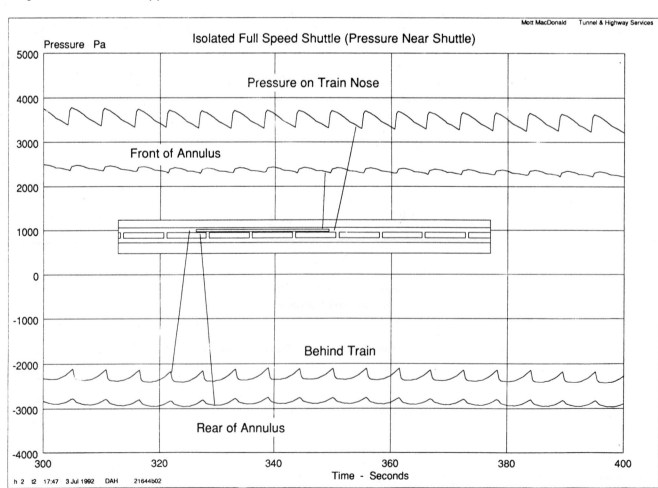

Figure 2   -   Full Speed Shuttle

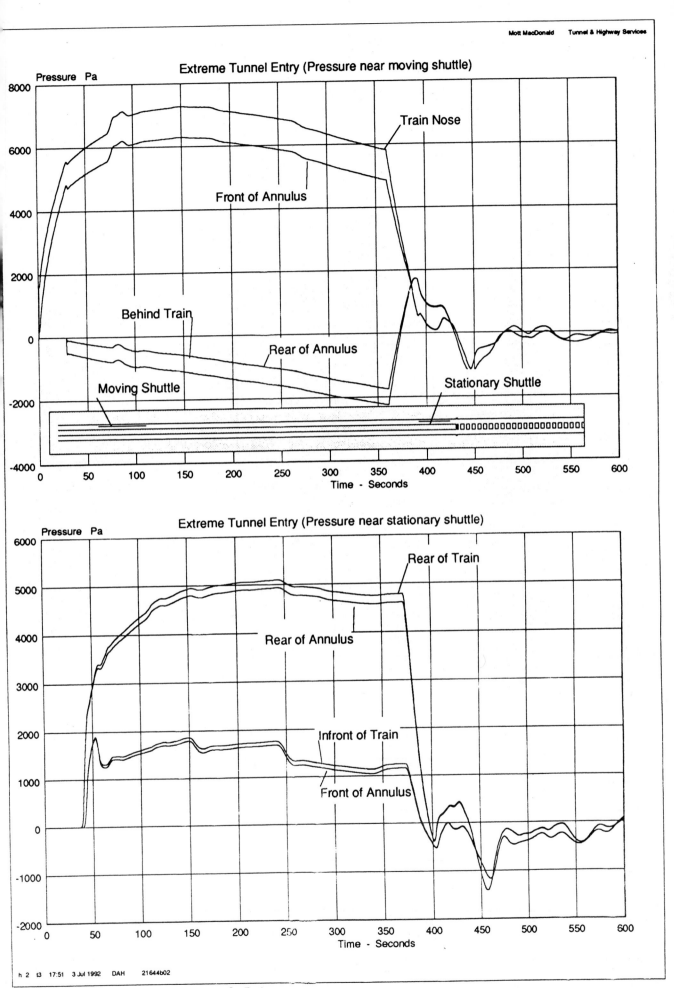

Mott MacDonald   Tunnel & Highway Services

Extreme Tunnel Entry (Pressure near moving shuttle)

Pressure Pa

Train Nose

Front of Annulus

Behind Train

Rear of Annulus

Moving Shuttle

Stationary Shuttle

Time - Seconds

Extreme Tunnel Entry (Pressure near stationary shuttle)

Pressure Pa

Rear of Train

Rear of Annulus

Infront of Train

Front of Annulus

Time - Seconds

h 2 t3 17:51 3 Jul 1992 DAH 21644b02

Figure 3 - Extreme Tunnel Entry
(a & b)

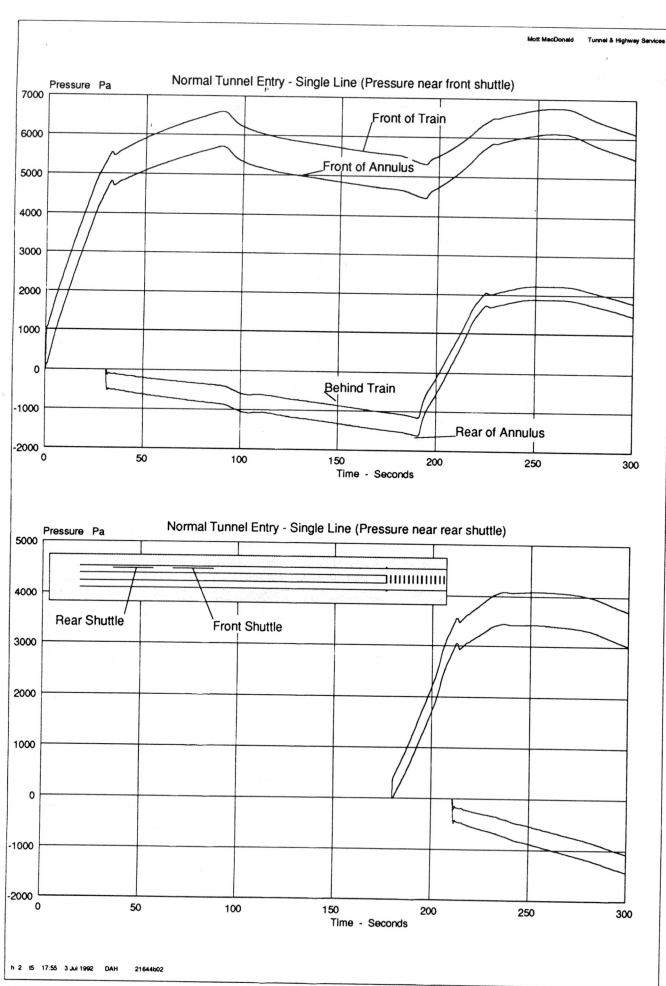

Normal Tunnel Entry - Single Line (Pressure near front shuttle)

Pressure Pa

Front of Train

Front of Annulus

Behind Train

Rear of Annulus

Time - Seconds

Normal Tunnel Entry - Single Line (Pressure near rear shuttle)

Pressure Pa

Rear Shuttle

Front Shuttle

Time - Seconds

h 2 t5 17:55 3 Jul 1992   DAH   21644b02

Figure 5   –   Normal Tunnel Entry (Single Line)
(a & b)

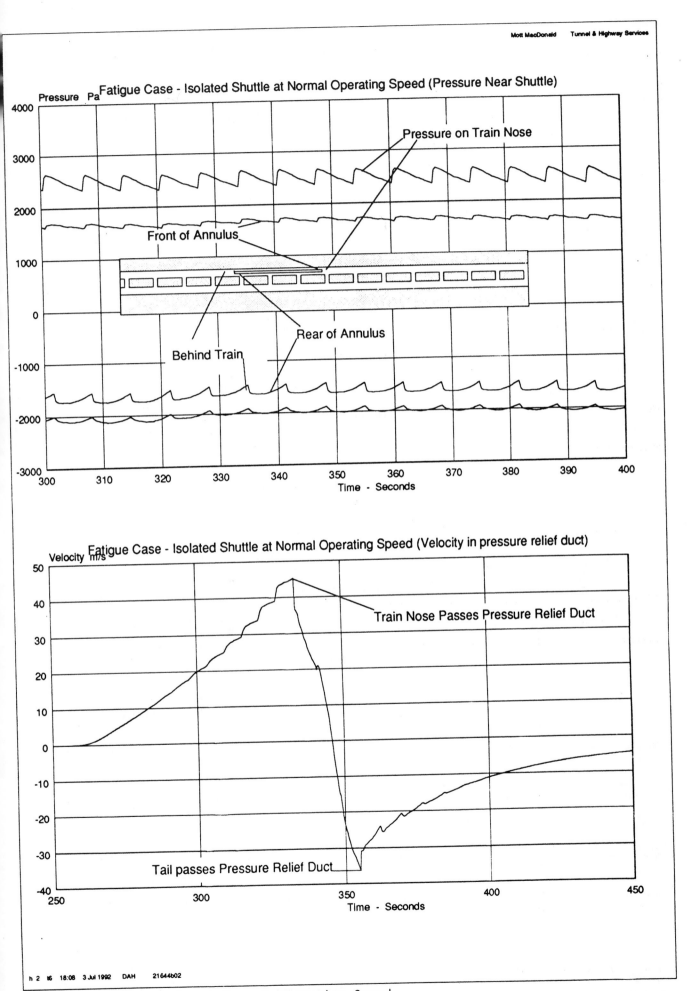

Figure 6 – Shuttle at Normal Operating Speed
(a & b)

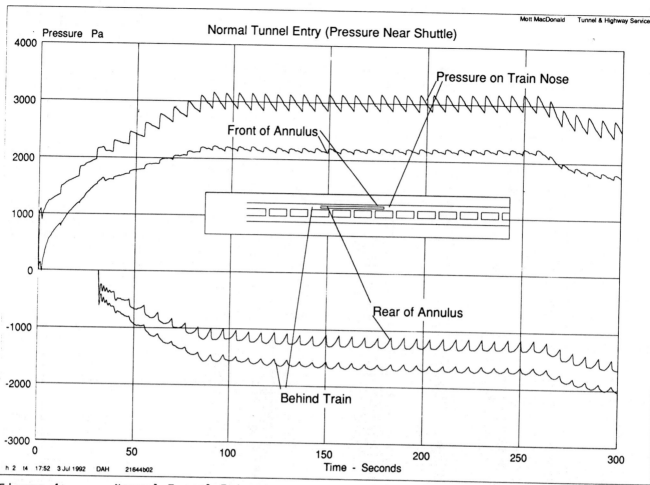

Figure 4   –   Normal Tunnel Entry

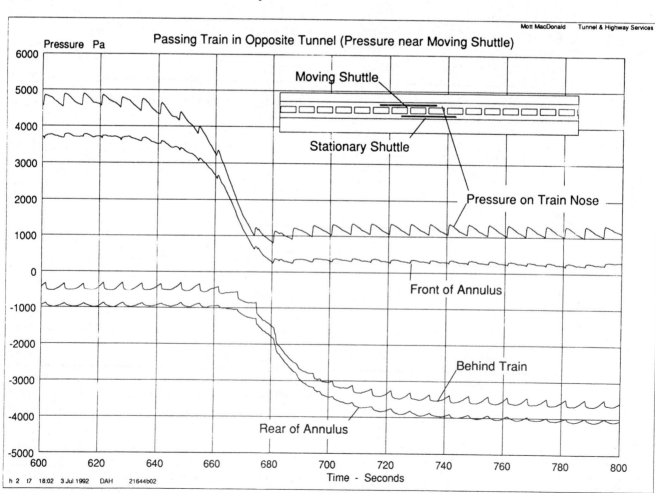

Figure 7   –   Shuttle passing at Normal Operating Speed

Appendix A1. Assumptions taken for this paper

Tunnel length	= 50000m
Tunnel free area	= 42.2m
Tunnel perimeter	= 26.81m
Tunnel friction coefficient	= 0.00916
Pressure relief duct loss coefficient	= 1.8
Distance between PR ducts	= 250m
Shuttle length	= 790m
Shuttle effective area	= 21.2m
Shuttle perimeter	= 18.0m
Shuttle nose coefficient	= 0.23
Inside wagon length	= 25m
Inside wagon width	= 4m
Inside wagon deck height	= 2m
Number of decks	= 2
Effective leakage per deck	= 0.02m^2
Maximum bellows length	= 1.4m
Minimum bellows length	= 1.25m
Halon stock per deck	= 67 kg
(Release time of	10s)
Typical entry speed	= 80kph
Maximum entry speed	= 100kph
Single line operation speed	= 100kph
Typical operation speed	= 135kph
Design speed	= 160kph

Appendix A2.

Operating   Circumstances   and   Simulation Predictions

Seven operating circumstances have been simulated, using the Compressible Flow network programme, as a basis for the calculations reported in this paper. These seven cases are now identified.

A2.1   Stopped Shuttle Case. A shuttle in one tunnel, at a constant speed of 160kph, passes a shuttle which is stopped in the other tunnel. All pressure relief ducts are open and the crossovers are closed.

This simulation results in a representative extreme pressure relief duct velocity which allows determination of the corresponding local pressure loads on the shuttle. This maximum velocity occurs at the first pressure relief duct after the stopped shuttle and is directed towards the moving shuttle. Figure 1 shows the velocity history at this PRD.

A2.2   Isolated Full Speed Shuttle. A single shuttle is operating at a constant speed of 160kph. All pressure relief ducts are open and the crossovers are closed.

This simulation results in a representative extreme pressure difference from front to back of the shuttle. Figure 2 indicates these pressures. (The small fluctuations are associated with passing pressure relief ducts)

A2.3   Extreme Tunnel Entry. A shuttle enters a single line working section at 100kph; it maintains this speed until 10km and then decelerates to a stop. This entry transient effects another shuttle stopped (at 15km) shortly before the first crossover. Pressure relief ducts are closed to the first crossover and then open beyond that. The first crossover is open.

This simulation results in representative extreme transients. Figure 3a shows pressure fluctuations around the stationary shuttle and figure 3b shows those around the moving shuttle.

A2.4   Normal Tunnel Entry. A shuttle enters a tunnel at 80kph and then accelerates up to a constant speed of 135 kph. All pressure relief ducts are open and the crossovers are closed.

This simulation results in representative typical entry transients associated with normal day time operation. These are shown as Figure 4.

A2.5   Normal Tunnel Entry (Single Line). A shuttle enters at 80kph and then accelerates to a constant speed of 100kph. Its entry transient affects another shuttle which is 3 minutes ahead of it. The pressure relief ducts are closed to the first crossover and open thereafter. The first crossover is open.

This simulation results in representative typical entry transients. Figure 5a shows pressure fluctuations around the front shuttle and figure 5b those around the rear shuttle.

A2.6   Isolated shuttle at normal operating speed

A single shuttle is operating at a constant speed of 135kph. All pressure relief ducts are open and the crossovers are closed.

This simulation results in typical pressure regimes and flow velocities. Figure 6a shows the pressure around the shuttle. Figure 6b gives the corresponding pressure relief duct velocities.

A2.7   Shuttle passing at normal operating speed

A shuttle operating at a constant speed of 135 kph is passed by a shuttle in the other tunnel at the same speed. All pressure relief ducts are open and the crossovers are closed.

This simulation results in typical pressure and airflow fluctuations as shuttles pass. Figure 6 shows the pressure fluctuation around one of the shuttles. Rather interestingly pressure differences past the shuttle, and PRD velocities, both fall as shuttles cross.

Appendix A3   Methods of Analysis

A3.1   Compressible Flow Network Programme

The calculations to show the pressure changes in the tunnels caused by the piston action of the trains have been done using the Mott MacDonald Tunnel Aerodynamics Computer program (which is described in Henson DA and Fox JA "Transient Flows in Tunnel Complexes of the type proposed for the Channel Tunnel" proceedings of IMechE 188 15/74). This program uses compressible, unsteady flow theory and the equations are solved using the Method of Characteristics. Data is prepared to specify to the program the system geometry, including tunnel areas, perimeters and friction factors, together with details of pressure relief ducts, crossovers etc. Train lengths, areas, perimeter, loss coefficients and detailed information on speed variation with time are also input.

The program divides the tunnel network into a grid of points and the equations are solved at each grid point at small time step intervals, typically 0.1 to 0.3 seconds. Special provision is made for the moving trains. The program thus produces the air pressure and velocity in all parts of the tunnel network varying with time. Other output provides the train drag, and power needed to overcome it, and results are produced both numerically and graphically as required.

The program has been used extensively in the design of the Channel Tunnel and in many other main line and rapid transit systems world-wide and has been verified against measurements taken in tunnels and models on many occasions.

A3.2 Calculation of Pressure Equalisation through a 'Leaky Box'

The wagon is considered to be a leaky box, through which air will flow in response to a pressure difference between the inside and the outside. The free volume within the box and the leakage area is accounted for. The leakage is assumed to act as an orifice with a discharge coefficient of 0.6. The compression or expansion of the air in the box is assumed to be adiabatic.

The analysis results in the following equations:

$$\frac{dP_i}{dt} = \frac{C_D A \gamma}{\frac{1}{2}\rho_o V} (P_o - P_i)^{\frac{1}{2}} P_o \qquad \text{A3.2.1}$$

for external pressure > internal pressure, and

$$\frac{dP_i}{dt} = \frac{C_D A \gamma}{\frac{1}{2}\rho_i V} (P_i - P_o)^{\frac{1}{2}} P_i \qquad \text{A3.2.2}$$

for internal pressure > external pressure.

The pressure outside the box is defined as a function of time by the compressible flow network program (Appendix 3.1). These equations are then solved using a Taylor approximation.

A3.3 Calculation of the pressure increase due to Halon release.

This calculation accounts for several effects:

1. The addition of the Halon into the wagon increases the internal pressure,

2. The Halon and air mixture leaks out of the wagon under the pressure difference between inside and outside.

3. The pressure outside the wagon is different on the front, sides and rear, due to the longitudinal pressure gradient created by the forward motion of the wagon

4. The latent heat of vaporisation of the Halon is supplied by the air in the wagon, and the wagon walls and contents, causing a cooling of the air,

5. The enthalpy of the air is considered, taking into account its relative humidity.

The Halon and air is assumed to be well mixed in the wagon. In practice, stratification will occur due to the relative densities of Halon and air, and the movement of air through the wagon. This could result in a more rapid loss of Halon from the rear of the wagon.

The total amount of Halon, and its rate of addition, is specified.

The calculation proceeds as follows.

At a given time after release of Halon, the pressure in the wagon is given by,

$$P_i = \left(\frac{M_H Z_H}{m_H} + \frac{M_a Z_a}{m_a} \right) \frac{RT}{V} \qquad \text{A 3.3.1}$$

The heat balance equation below is used to calculate the change in temperature, ΔT, during a time interval Δt.

$$C_{V_a} M_a \Delta T + M_W L_W + C_{V_H} M_H \Delta T + C_B \Delta T = \frac{dM_H}{dt} L_H \Delta t$$

$$\text{A 3.3.2}$$

The volume flow rate through each of the wagon walls is given by equation A3.2.2 above.

Using a Taylor approximation, the mass of Halon and air remaining in the wagon is calculated, the hence the pressure, by equation A3.3.1

A3.4 Calculation of pressure loads in the event of a fire

The wagons are required to have a fire resistance time of at least 30 minutes to prevent the spread of smoke along the train in the event of a fire occurring on board. An assessment of the pressure loads due to rapid thermal expansion which could occur during this time is made.

If there were a fire, it would supply heat to the body of the wagon, and its contents, which would heat the air in the wagon by convection. This mechanism is described by the following equation.

$$\text{FIRE POWER} = C_B \frac{dT_B}{dt} + \left(\frac{k N_u A_s}{L} \right) (T_B - T_a)$$

$$\text{A 3.4.1}$$

Values for the heat transfer coefficient $(k N_u A_s / L)$ and the wagon heat capacity, C_B, were obtained by consideration of tests carried out at the Fire Research Station.

For a given fire growth rate, the temperature of the air in the wagon, and hence its pressure, can be calculated. Flow of air out of the wagon, due to leakage is calculated by the method of Appendix A3.2.

© IMechE 1992 C451/033

Note that similar calculations have been done which accounted for the combined effects of fire and Halon release.

A3.5 Calculations of Pressure Loads due to coupler compression

Shunting and braking dynamics can result in rapid changes from traction to compression between wagons. Correspondingly the coupler system can change rapidly between its fully extended and its fully compressed length. The proportional change in bellows length (measured from fire barrier to fire barrier) being around 10%.

If the bellows could concertiner without any slack in the fabric, and were made of inelastic materials, the adiabatic pressure change would be given by

$$P_F - P_{in} = \left(\frac{l_{in}}{l_F}\right)^\gamma - 1 \qquad \text{A3.5.1}$$

The pressure change (and load) from real bellows would be less because the bellows will have slack and stretch, because the length change is not instantaneous, and because there is leakage.

The actual pressure transient is very dependent on the details of the bellows design. For the purpose of this paper, the pressure change is simply taken as one quarter of the value obtained by the above simplified analysis.

The structural pressure load on the bellows and fire barriers is equal to this pressure charge.

The fatigue load is still more difficult to assess. For this paper it has been taken as a fifth of the extreme load acting 10 times per two-way transit.

A3.6 Local Pressure Effects

The effects of the air flow through the piston relief ducts, impinging on the shuttle wagon, is to create an increased pressure loading. This pressure is proportional to the dynamic head of the air flow, ie.

pressure = C_p x dynamic head

The factor C_p is dependent on the velocity profile across the duct area, and takes different values depending on the direction of air flow in the PRD. The C_p is assumed to be 1.1 when the flow is towards the wagon, and 0.2 when it is away.

APPENDIX A4
Notation used in the Appendices

A	leakage area of wagon	m^2
C_B	heat capacity of wagon body and contents	kJ/K
C_v	specific heat capacity at constant volume	kJ/kg K
C_D	discharge coefficient for leakage area	
M	mass of gas in volume	kg
m	molecular weight	kg/kmol
P	pressure	Pa
R	gas constant	kJ/kmol K
T	temperature	K
V	free volume in wagon	m^3
Z	compressibility factor in equation of state	
ρ	density	kg/m^3
γ	ratio of specific heats	
$\left(\dfrac{kN_uA_s}{L}\right)$	heat transfer coefficient in fire calculation	kJ/K

subscripts

a	air		i	internal
B	wagon body and contents		o	external
H	halon		in	initial
w	water vapour		f	final

The Channel Tunnel project constitution

P M MIDDLETON, CEng, FIMechE
W S Atkins and Partners, Epsom, Surrey

Introduction

Building and operating a major infrastructure project linking two countries is, of necessity, complex. Harmonisation of legislation through Brussels for the European community has not yet formalised such aspects as Health and Safety or indeed many other aspects of major engineering investment.

There have been a number of such Projects in the recent past. The general pattern has been to reach some form of political agreement and then to follow this with the setting up of an Inter Governmental Commission responsible to ensure that the interests and requirements of both countries involved are respected. A typical example of this approach is seen in the Frejus Road Tunnel project between France and Italy.

The Channel Tunnel is technically much more complex than any of these initiatives so far attempted in that it involves road and rail transport and at least half of the traffic running through the tunnel will continue on to National Rail Systems.

This paper describes the various formal agreements between the parties to the project as they exist today and traces the history of the development of this constitution with a particular emphasis on the aspect of Safety.

During the design and construction phase two aspects of Safety are described. Firstly construction safety and secondly the approach through design to the operational safety of the system. After commissioning the responsibility for safety of the system passes from the Contractor to the Employer and there is a change in organisation to match the new needs.

The Formation of the Project

The Project has a long history of almost 200 years and a number of attempts have been made to build a link between France and England. The present Project has it's roots in the 1972 scheme abandoned in 1974 after the election of a Labour Government in the UK.

Interest did not die amongst the contractor and the Banks and there was a continuous dialogue between interested parties. In 1982 the Governments asked the Banks to prepare a report on the subject with particular emphasis on the problem of finance. The report was issued in 1984 and suggested a political and financial framework for the Project. The financial framework proposed was not completely acceptable to the Governments who were looking for the Project to be financed in the private sector.

After further discussion the French and British Governments issued an enquiry in early 1985 for a Fixed Link to be financed in the private sector and asked for responses from interested parties to be put before them in the autumn of 1985.

The enquiry was based upon a concession to be granted to the successful proposer and an offer from the Governments to ensure the necessary treaty and legislation were put in place to allow the the project to proceed. The general framework proposed was that included in the Banks reports to which reference has already been made.

Submissions were made to the Governments at the end of October 1985 and in February 1986 the tunnel proposal put forward by CTG/FM was chosen. At this stage four important documents existed.

- The report of the Banks. (1)

  This report contained a proposal in some detail of the approach which could be adopted to the early political procedures.

- The enquiry document from the Governments. (2)

  The enquiry document invited bids for the Concession for a Fixed Link across the Channel and gave the political criteria that were to be met.

- The submission to the Governments. (3)

  This document contained amongst other things a technical description of a scheme based upon the 1974 project, an early draft of the construction contracts and proposals for funding the Project in the private sector.

- The decision of the governments presented to Parliament in February 1984. (4)

  This document sets out the way ahead for the legislative process in the UK. A similar document was published in France.

The Treaty (5)

During 1985-86 and in parallel with the preparation of the submissions by the Contractors and the Banks, the two Governments were discussing a Treaty designed to confirm the political will to ensure that the project was built. The Treaty was signed at Canterbury on 12th February 1986.

The Treaty gives the Government's powers (Article 7) to make arrangements specific to the Tunnel for Health and Safety. It also defines the terms of reference of an Inter Governmental Commission (IGC) (Article 10) and a Safety Authority (SA) (Article 11).

The IGC is set up to supervise the construction and operation of the Fixed Link on behalf of the Governments. The SA is required to advise the Inter Governmental Commission particularly on the subject of Safety both of Construction and Operation.

There followed a period of intense activity in which negotiations took place resulting in a number of significant agreements, each recorded in a formal document described below establishing the Constitution of the Project.

- The Concession agreement was signed in April 1986. (6)

- In the UK a Hybrid Bill was presented to Parliament and this became an Act in 1987 allowing the Treaty to be ratified by the UK Government. (7)

- In France a similar process led to the Declaration d'Utilitie Publique allowing the Treaty to be ratified by the French Government.

- Preparations were made for the Loan Agreement with the Banks. (8)

- The Construction Contract was negotiated in detail and signed on 13th August 1986. (9)

- The duties and role of the Maitre d'Oeuvre (Independent Project Managers) were negotiated and a contract written and signed on 13th July 1986. (10)

Each of these documents will be taken in turn.

The Concession Agreement

This agreement between the Government and the owner CTG/FM (Later Eurotunnel) sets out in some detail the rights and duties of the Inter Governmental Commission and Safety Authority in the one hand and Eurotunnel on the other.

Chapter II of this document describes the responsibilities of the parties with regard to Safety, Security and the Environment. It also establishes the position of the MdO and describes the role required of that organisation in relationship to the Project.

The IGC and the Safety Authority have between them a duty to the Governments defined in the treaty and the concession to monitor Construction Safety. In the UK this responsibility is delegated internally within Government Circles to the Health and Safety Executive and this is effective for those parts of the work which are clearly under UK Jurisdiction. The concession also puts a duty on the MdO to monitor and report to the IGC on Construction Safety Matters. This is not limited to one country but is on a bi-national basis.

The Channel Tunnel Act (7)

The Hybrid Bill established the general consent for the construction of the Tunnel and its infrastructure in Kent near to Folkestone and Dover. It also defined the works required to connect the tunnel project to the London Terminal situated at Waterloo. The passage of the Bill through parliament was achieved in time through two committees - one in the Commons and one in the Lords as is usual for many Bills. The public were encouraged to present their views.

In the process there was much discussion on the question of safety with particular reference to the problem of accompanied traffic. This was the start of the so-called "non segregation" debate.

In the course of this process the SA was given the power to bypass the IGC and return to parliament should they feel strongly on an issue.

The Act was passed in July 1987.

The Loan Agreement (8)

The loan agreement between the Banks and Eurotunnel sets down conditions for providing a loan for the construction and operation of the Project.

It completes the overall structure of the constitution of the Project and confirms its interests in the general performance of the Project. The Banks are interested in a good safety organisation not only on an intrinsic basis but also from the point of view of making satisfactory progress in construction and continuous operation in revenue earning service.

The Construction Contract (9)

The Construction Contract requires, as is normal, that the Contractor is responsible for all Construction Safety matters and in this respect the HSE performs its normal function.

Eurotunnel is required, in the same contract, as Employer, to ensure that the contractor is performing his duties. As explained later the Contractor TML is not a legal entity in the UK so that any legal sanctions taken by the HSE have to be taken against the consortium forming the UK half of TML. Various prosecutions have been heard.

The contractor has taken this responsibility very seriously and has developed an attitude to Safety within his own staff and his subcontractor which is at the forefront of modern practice. As an example of this attitude, the approach to eye safety has had remarkable results which should be an example to all.

The MdO Contract (10)

The MdO role is akin to Technical Auditor for the Channel Tunnel Project. As part of its duty the MdO is required to review all submissions made by Eurotunnel to the IGC/SA with a particular view to safety. They are also required to witness the construction and commissioning of the works on behalf of the IGC/SA and finally to make recommendations for the issue of the operating certificate. These duties amongst others are defined in the MdO contract existing between Eurotunnel and the Atkins Setec joint venture.

With this historical background and the description of the various agreements in mind the relationship between the parties can now be considered for the two phases of the project.

Construction Phase

The organisation for construction safety is different on each side of the Channel and this paper will deal only with the bi-national and UK organisation.

The agreements already described in some detail above, taken together, produce a complex interaction between the Parties.

The overall organisation of the Project is shown at figure 1. In figure 2 the links between the major players are shown.

Enough has already been said to enable these diagrams to be readily understood.

It is necessary to expand the organisation of the Contractor TML in order to understand their legal position in front of Health and Safety legislation in each of the countries. TML is a joint venture of two groups of contracting companies centred in the UK and France respectively and is not a legal entity in its own right. The UK companies are a consortium of Balfour Beatty: Costain, Taylor Woodrow, Tarmac and Wimpey. This organisation is shown in figure 3.

Figure 4 shows this construction safety operating organisation in some detail. During the early stages of the construction it was simple to allow the normal statutory safety systems to work in the UK and France quite separately. Thus the HSE and other statutory bodies performed their normal duty as shown in the left hand column of figure 4. The IGC/SA and MdO maintained a monitoring role which took account of the national norms.

The two halves of the Project are now connected and it is gradually becoming more and more integrated. This has put emphasis on a joint approach to many aspects of construction and the IGC/SA is gradually becoming more involved. During the commissioning phase when trains are running in the tunnel and the Contractor is still responsible for safety under the construction contract further integration of the two sides will be required.

Operational Safety

The responsibility for safety of the transport system, road and rail within the perimeter fence in UK and France including the tunnels rests with Eurotunnel. During the construction phase the design construction and safety arrangements are submitted to the IGC/SA for non-objection supported by a detailed review and report made by the MdO. Independent committees, chaired by the MdO review the signalling and control and communications systems to ensure the highest safety standards.

The SA, is assisted in its task in the UK by the Railway Inspectorate now part of the HSE, and other bodies such as the Police and Kent Fire Brigade. Interested Government Departments are also represented.

Before the system can be put into operation, Eurotunnel must obtain an Operating Certificate from the Governments through the IGC. Test during the commissioning stage will be witnessed in detail by the MdO who will issue a recommendation that the Certificate be issued.

The condition for the issue of this certificate will be based upon the following criteria.

a) That the Project has been built in accordance with the design presented to the IGC/SA and to which they have "no objections".

b) That the national and international standards defined in the above submission and supporting documents have been met.

c) That the individual items of equipment have achieved their specified performance and safety criteria.

d) That subsystems operate to their specified performance and safety criteria.

e) That the transportation system as a whole meets the requirements of the systems design and conforms to a developed and agreed safety case. The system must be capable of being operated within the terms of the operation procedures described in (g) below.

f) That the statutory standards of the relevant country have been met and where both countries are affected that a joint standard is agreed and met.

g) That the transportation system as commissioned is represented in the safety case and complies with safety case requirements.

h) That the appropriate project records, operating rules and maintenance manuals are available.

i) That there is an appropriate statutory regulation specifying the precise conditions under which the transportation system may be operated. The form of these regulations is yet to be defined.

j)   That the operating rules and emergency procedures have been approved by the IGC.

k)   That the rules for the transport of dangerous goods have bee approved by the IGC.

The Safety case detailed in the above criteria is the summation of all the safety aspects of the various systems involved in the operation of the project. In risk terms the safety objectives are based on equal or better criteria than those used for equivalent railway systems.

The HSE and other statutory bodies will have their normal role with regards to operatives in the UK. Special arrangements will be made for those operatives working on a bi-national basis (Anglo-French).

The organisation for the operational stage is still under discussion but figure 5 gives an indication likely relationships after the final Operations Certificate is in place.

Conclusion

Both Construction and Operational Safety for the Channel Tunnel Project has been in the forefront of the organisation. The approach has been necessarily complex in that there are many interested parties and the project itself has many different technical facets.

This Constitution is therefore complex. This paper gives the framework within which other submissions to this conference can be better understood.

'References'

(1) 'Finance for a Fixed Channel Link'.

Proposed by the Franco-British Channel Link financing Group 1984.

(2) Invitation to Promoters 2nd April 1985.

(Official Journal of the European communities C172/5 7th September 1985).

(3) Submission to the Governments dated 30th October 1985.

Submitted by Channel Tunnel Group and France Manche.

(4) The Channel Fixed Link(3)

HMSO Command 9735 February 1986.

(5) Treaty between the United Kingdom of Great Britain and Northern Ireland and the French Republic concerning the construction and operation by Private Concessionaires of a Channel Fixed Link (Canterbury 12th February 1986) HMSO Command 9745.

(6) The Channel Fixed Link

Concession Agreement (14th March 1986) HMSO Command 9769.

(7) The Channel Tunnel Act 1987

HMSO ISBN 0105453870

(8) Credit Agreement existing between of the Eurotunnel and the Banks and signed first in November 1987.

(9) Construction Contract

Signed between Eurotunnel and Transmanche Link on 13th August 1986.

(10) Maitre d'Oeuvre Contract

Signed 13th August 1986.

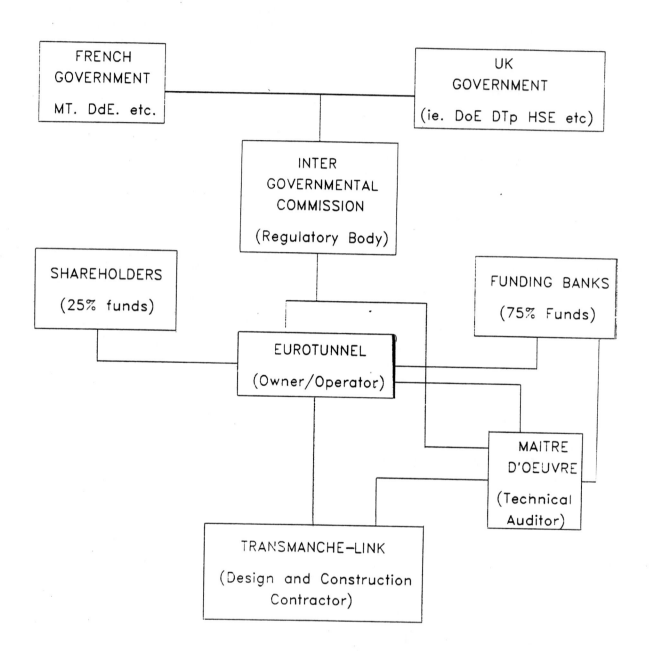

Figure 1.
General Organisation of the Project

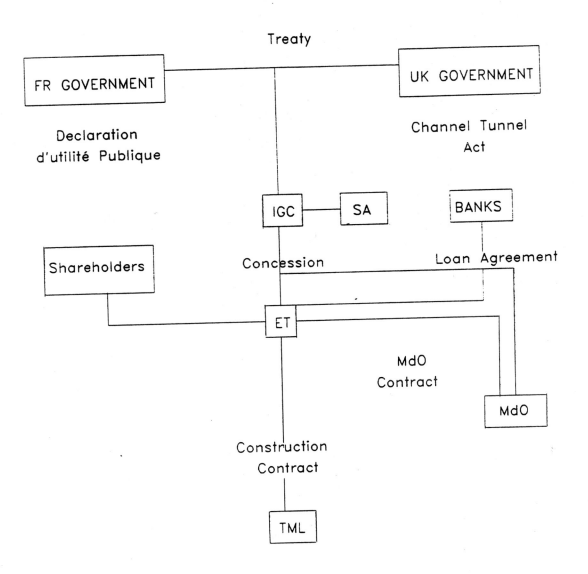

Figure 2.
Organisation of the Project
with Agreements identified

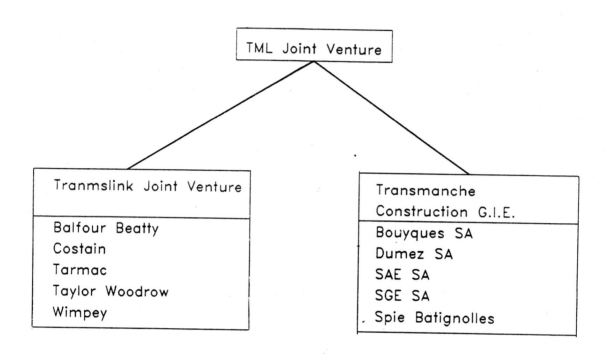

Figure 3.
The Contractor Organisation

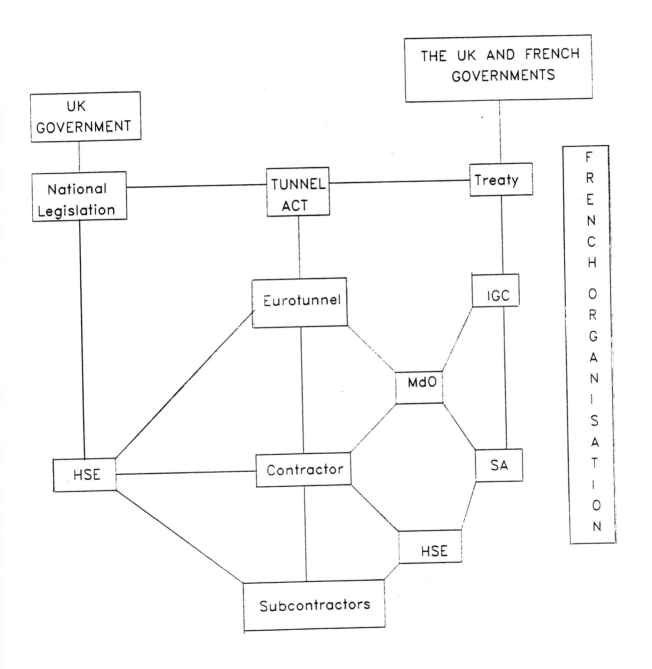

Figure 4.
UK Construction Safety Organisation

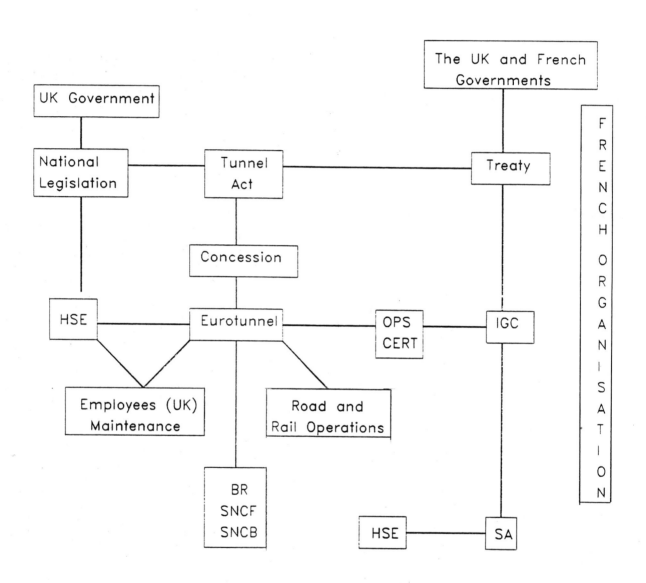

Figure 5.
The UK Operational Safety Organisation

The development of standard responses for emergency incidents in the Channel Tunnel

J COPE, BA, MCIT and S E FRENCH, BSc
Kennedy Henderson Limited, Godalming, Surrey

SYNOPSIS

This paper describes the methodology used to prepare standard responses for emergency incidents in the Channel Tunnel. Initially, work was directed at identifying hazards arising from tunnel operation, understanding tunnel behaviour under emergency conditions and preparing tunnel safety studies on topics such as evacuation. A technique was developed to bind all these elements together and from this, it was possible to define overall objectives for handling tunnel incidents, and to derive standard responses to those incidents. The paper contains some examples of standard responses and concludes by drawing together the various elements to illustrate the overall methodology.

INTRODUCTION

Every railway administration in the world devotes time and resources to planning for events that will never happen. Nevertheless, the occurrence of the occasional severe incident, e.g. the collisions at Gare de Lyon and Clapham Junction, serves as a reminder of the need for a constant state of preparedness, and the availability of a standard response sequence that can be implemented almost immediately, providing a framework which can be used as a guide to the actions of operating personnel involved in the handling of emergency incidents.

The need to prepare pre-determined response sequences to deal with emergencies in the Channel Tunnel was recognised at an early stage and this paper provides an outline of the methodology and techniques employed to meet this objective and that of providing a basis for the preparation of a comprehensive set of emergency procedures.

OBJECTIVE OF SIMPLE PRE-DETERMINED PROCEDURES

The Channel Tunnel will have a number of characteristics, the combination of which will make it unlike any other railway in the world:

- 2 x 50km running tunnels plus 50km service tunnel;
- intensive train service operating on close headways;
- presence of motor vehicles on many trains;
- large numbers of people within the system at any one time;
- mixture of train types (passenger shuttle, HGV shuttle, international freight and passenger)

However, the fact that the Channel Tunnel is being designed and built as a new transport system in its own right, enables Eurotunnel to incorporate in it a level of safety provision which would be difficult to achieve in existing systems. A wide range of safety features has been built into the design of the transportation system, which will ensure that the occurrence of any emergency incident is a remote possibility. The system is also designed to mitigate the consequences of any incident, however unlikely. Despite the high intrinsic safety of the system, Eurotunnel, as a responsible operator, together with the tunnel's designer and builder Transmanche-Link, identified at an early stage the need to prepare procedures to deal with all types of emergency incident in the tunnel, however remote the possibility of occurrence. Furthermore, it was considered that because of the unique characteristics of the tunnel, it would be beneficial to structure the response to emergency incidents in such a way that operators could implement a pre-determined routine at the outset, with the objective of getting the process of incident-handling off to a good start.

The remainder of this paper will describe the process by which a 'standard' response was prepared and tested, through the undertaking of an in-depth analysis of the technical aspects of the transportation system incorporating tunnel design and operation. Two key questions had to be answered:-

(i) what was the range of emergency incidents that might be envisaged in the tunnel?

(ii) what constraints would the tunnel itself impose on the handling of an emergency incident?

RANGE OF INCIDENTS TO BE ASSESSED

In order to ensure that the full range of incidents for which an emergency response might be necessary could be determined, a comprehensive hazard analysis of the transportation system was undertaken. At an early stage it was recognised that the hazards that might be anticipated in the terminals were largely different to those that might be anticipated in the tunnels. This was due not only to the obvious differences in environment, but also to the different operations taking place in each part of the system. Whilst this paper focuses on hazards in the tunnel, those which are relevant to the terminals have also been analysed by Eurotunnel.

The hazard analysis was prepared in a conventional manner, with the detail of the design and proposed operation of the tunnel and terminals being reviewed to establish:

-   what were the hazards;
-   what elements of the design were intended to prevent the occurrence of the hazard;
-   what elements of the design might ameliorate the hazard;
-   where operating procedures were intended to act as the response to the occurrence of a hazard.

By definition, a hazard analysis is comprehensive. Thus the range of hazards identified included collisions, derailments, fires and floods at the extreme end of the scale, and involving a potentially large number of people, right through to single events with potentially serious consequences for the individual, such as electrocution, or being bitten by an unspecified animal!

The completion of the hazard analysis meant that one of the two elements necessary for the preparation of emergency procedures had been put in place. An example of a page from the hazard analysis is included as Figure 1.

THE INFLUENCE OF ROLLING STOCK AND INFRASTRUCTURE DESIGN ON PROCEDURES

The design of the different types of rolling stock using the tunnel was a key input to the preparation of emergency procedures. The Tourist Shuttle trains are designed to a very high safety specification and the safety features incorporated influenced the overall objectives of the response to emergency incidents. Key elements of the design are:

-   a locomotive at each end of every shuttle train. One locomotive alone will be capable of pulling the entire shuttle out of the tunnel;

-   provision of a comprehensive fire detection and extinguishing system onboard each carrier wagon;

-   fire barrier at both ends of every wagon (each fire barrier is fitted with two pass-doors to facilitate the rapid evacuation of a wagon in the event of fire);

-   wagons designed to resist an internal fire for 30 minutes;

-   a wagon ventilation system which can be shut down in the event of an internal fire. Should smoke enter the tunnel, ventilation systems can be operated in such a way that air is not drawn into the shuttle interior;

-   emergency lighting;

-   sophisticated communications and control systems.

The different design of the HGV shuttle and the fact that lorry drivers are to be conveyed separately from their vehicles was also taken into account.

The requirement to produce emergency procedures also necessitated a good understanding of the tunnel environment. Much of the work that was called upon as input to the preparation of the procedures had already been commissioned as part of a wider need to assess the various engineering and operational considerations that needed to be taken into account in the design of a long undersea tunnel. It is not possible within the confines of this short paper to list all of the background studies that were used, but the following paragraphs highlight one or two that were particularly relevant.

Tunnel Ventilation Studies

A series of studies was commissioned by Eurotunnel/TML to assess the implications of using the tunnel supplementary ventilation system during emergency incidents and how its use should be co-ordinated with the adjustment of the normal ventilation system, the opening and closing of cross passage doors and the movement of other trains in the tunnel.

Evacuation Studies

A series of evacuation studies was undertaken analysing the detail of the evacuation process in various stages, e.g.

-   within the train (away from the hazard);

-   from the train to the Service Tunnel;

-   from the Service Tunnel to the terminals via an evacuation train.

These studies provided a valuable insight into the deployment of staff under emergency evacuation conditions.

Non-segregation Studies

The 'non-segregation' studies were undertaken to demonstrate the level of safety inherent within the concept of conveying car and coach passengers with their vehicles.

This series of studies provided valuable information regarding safety on board shuttle trains, and an early indication of such key factors as the fire detection/suppression systems, availability of communication facilities on board the shuttle train, details of on-board services such as lighting, ventilation etc, crewing arrangements for shuttle trains and the duties of each member of the traincrew in emergencies.

In addition to the specific studies, examples of which have been listed above, other details were evolving which would provide valuable input. In particular, final detail was emerging on tunnel services such as lighting, pumping, cooling and drainage. Tunnel geography such as location of evacuation routes and running tunnel crossovers, and operating policy such as train timetabling and maintenance strategy was also taken into account in the consideration of procedures.

A means now had to be found to bind together the output from the hazard analysis with the information on the tunnel's technical characteristics into a format which could be used as the basis for developing standard responses, and at a later date, emergency procedures.

This need was addressed by means of the 'Emergency Situations Analysis'.

EMERGENCY SITUATIONS ANALYSIS

The Emergency Situations Analysis was developed jointly by Kennedy Henderson and their co-Consultants on safety studies, Société Générale de Techniques et d'Etudes (SGTE), of Paris. It took as its basis the hazards which had been identified in the Preliminary Hazard Analysis, and developed each of them into scenarios based upon details of system design, existing outline procedures and operations and maintenance policy. Two standard forms were developed, with one having the purpose of summarising the incident detail, and the other illustrating, in the form of a time history, how each incident might develop. Examples of these two forms are given as Figures 2 and 3.

The whole range of tunnel incidents was assessed from collision, derailment and fire, through to electrocution and pollution. The initial effects of the incident were analysed and the consequences of that incident then developed. The analysis looked at the principal participants in the handling of tunnel incidents, i.e. the Railway Control Centre, the traincrew and passengers on both the incident train and on other trains in the tunnel at the time of the incident, and the emergency services (both ET and National agencies). As well as the human elements, tunnel engineering systems and train movements could also be represented by means of the dedication of particular columns on the analysis forms.

The reason for adopting this technique was to model the dependencies which might exist in any emergency situation, to highlight the need for communication links and items of equipment (and to ensure that they had been provided in the design) and to gain an appreciation of the kinds of activity that might need to take place, at each stage in the development of the incident. The latter was considered particularly important, and the production of an incident time history was beneficial in identifying the responsibilities that would fall to the traincrew and Control Centre staff in the early stages of an incident when the emergency services were en route to the incident site.

A significant number of emergency situations were analysed. In so doing, particular attention was paid to the emergence of common actions, especially in the early stages of an incident, irrespective of its nature or detail. Whilst it would not be expected that one response would be found to be standard for all incidents ranging from electrocution to collision, the hope was that certain requirements would be found to be common to every incident involving trains in the running tunnels, such that standard responses for the initial phase of incident-handling could be developed. The remainder of this paper focuses on incidents involving trains in the running tunnels.

The scenarios promoted a wide-ranging consideration of the appropriateness of the tunnel design for emergency incident handling and were able to form valuable input into the development of emergency procedures.

The following sections describe in more detail the way in which the scenarios were used as the critical link between consideration of the hazards, and the foundation of procedures to cope with those hazards.

TOWARDS A STANDARD RESPONSE

So far this paper has described the ways in which analysis was undertaken to understand how the various components of the transportation system would interact in the event of an emergency. This process enabled the preparation of a series of scenarios to examine the development of a wide range of incidents (using the Emergency Situation Analysis technique). It was now felt necessary to define a series of general principles, common to all scenarios, which could be used to shape the procedural response. These general principles arose naturally from an analysis of the various scenarios involving trains, considered in the Emergency Situations Analysis. These were found to fall into two main categories:

Incidents occurring onboard moving trains in the tunnel[*1]

Important examples include;

- fire in a tourist shuttle

- fire on a locomotive

Serious incidents involving a train which is stopped (or stopping) as the consequence of an incident in the tunnel[*1]

Important examples include;

- derailment or collision

- uncontained fire which causes a train to stop in the tunnel

The general principles can be summarised as follows;

(a) **Incidents Occurring Onboard Moving Trains in the Tunnel**

- actions should be taken in accordance with a standard response thereby limiting the possibility for error or undue delay during the early stages of an incident

- remove passengers and staff from the vicinity of the hazard

- alert emergency personnel at the earliest opportunity

- whenever possible keep the incident train moving

- maximise the distance between the incident train and other trains in the tunnel

- configure the system in such a way that the worst possible outcome of the incident can be dealt with.

(b) **Serious Incidents Involving a Train which is Stopped (or Stopping) due to an Incident in the Tunnel**

- actions should be taken in accordance with a standard response.

- alert emergency personnel at the earliest opportunity.

[*1]The general principles identified in the case of an incident outside of the tunnel (eg during the loading and unloading phase) have also been defined. These are not considered within this paper.

- the aim of operators during the first minutes of a serious incident is to configure the system in such a way that conditions are suitable for a rapid evacuation of the incident train (should it prove necessary).

- passengers on the incident train to be removed from the vicinity of the hazard without delay.

- the occupants of other trains to be protected.

- the departure of other trains from the tunnel should not be unduly delayed.

- in the event that passengers and staff are required to leave their train, an alternative train should be made available as quickly as feasible.

- the eventual intervention of fire-fighting crews must be enabled.

- in overall terms the first priority must be the safety of passengers and staff. The limitation of damage to the tunnel and associated equipment is desirable but is clearly of lesser importance.

The general principles described above have formed the basis of the procedural response developed by Eurotunnel and the approach was verified by independent experts with relevant experience. The basic strategy has also been subject to the close scrutiny of the Channel Tunnel Safety Authority (SA), an organisation that was established to advise the Intergovernmental Commission (IGC) on matters relating to safety.

Identification of general principles was a necessary first step. However in order to achieve the ultimate objective (a safe operating regime) it is necessary to translate principles into actual procedures. This task is well progressed and the main elements of the standard response have been defined. These are of course subject to constant review to ensure the best possible match of procedures with the general principles outlined above.

THE STANDARD RESPONSE

The studies carried out in the design phase of the project had demonstrated the critical nature of decisions made at the early stage of a major incident. However it also became apparent that the early stages of an incident may feature one or more of the following characteristics:

- an unexpected occurrence, an unusual combination of events;

- lack of information as regards the incident, possibility of confusing messages;

- high stress for the staff concerned, high work-load;

- a rapidly developing sequence of events.

All of the above features will tend to reduce the probability of the railway controller correctly assessing the situation and taking the required action. For this reason it was soon recognised that the key to safety was the concept of the standard response. In simple terms the standard response is a list of actions which the operator is required to initiate in case of an emergency. As the name implies it is intended that the standard response for incidents on trains in the tunnel should, as far as possible, be invariable. This will mean that the operator is not required to choose which procedure to initiate, but instead must act in accordance with a defined list of actions regardless of the exact characteristics of the incident. The actions listed in the standard response are designed to address each of the general principles described previously and will therefore have the effect of placing the system in the configuration most conducive to safety. Once the standard response has been fully applied the operator will then be in a position to re-assess the situation and, if appropriate, begin to restore the system to normality. The overall approach can be summarised as follows:

TRIGGER EVENT (eg FIRE REPORTED)

IMPLEMENT STANDARD RESPONSE

REASSESS SITUATION

GRADUALLY RELAX OPERATIONAL CONSTRAINTS

RETURN TO NORMAL OPERATIONS

The standard response has two phases. The first relates to an incident on a moving train and the second relates to an incident on a train which is stopped or is about to stop. The first is designed in such a way that operators can switch smoothly to the second phase should it become apparent that a moving train must stop.

The main components of the standard response are shown below;

The Standard Response

Phase 1 - Incident on a Moving Train

Trigger Events

- fire reported on a moving train

- fire detected by tunnel-based fire detectors

- other event which gives rise to the possibility that the train may shortly become immobilised

Key Actions in Rough Order of Priority

(a) Stop trains behind the incident train

(b) Alert the Eurotunnel emergency crews (1st line response) and the national emergency services (2nd line response)

(c) Order all trains to slow to a pre-determined speed (this is done in order to allow for the closure of piston relief duct dampers)

(d) Order all trains to close their ventilation intake ducts

(e) Prevent further trains from entering the tunnel

(f) Close the piston relief duct dampers (thereby isolating the incident tunnel from the non-incident tunnel and preventing the further spread of smoke)

(g) Set the route into the emergency siding

(THE INCIDENT TRAIN CONTINUES IN TRANSIT)

Phase 2 - Incident on a Train which is Stopped or is about to Stop[*2]

Trigger Events

- a train with a fire onboard has been stopped (or is about to stop) in the tunnel

- a train has been stopped unexpectedly and the control centre cannot obtain an explanation from the train-crew

- a sudden event which immobilises the train (eg derailment)

[*2]Whenever a train is required to stop due to an incident onboard, the driver will always endeavour to bring it to a stand in such a position that the main evacuation doors are well placed for passenger evacuation, should it prove necessary.

Key Actions in Rough Order of Priority

Actions (a) - (e) of phase 1 PLUS ,,

(h) Stop all trains in the incident tunnel (this will have the effect of reducing air velocities in the incident tunnel thereby allowing the activation of Supplementary Ventilation System fans and the opening of crosspassage doors should either be required.)

(i) Prepare stopped trains behind the incident for reversal

(j) Determine the exact stopping position of the incident train, advise the emergency teams accordingly

(k) Activate high level lighting

(l) Where appropriate initiate the automatic decoupling procedure on the incident train

(m) Prepare an evacuation train (an empty tourist shuttle)

It is clear from the above that in operational terms both phases of the standard response are highly restrictive (ie they will cause considerable disruption to railway operations during the time taken to restore normality). However all of the actions specified are necessary in order that the worst possible outcomes of the incident can be allowed for. In this way the highest possible level of safety can be achieved for the full range of scenarios previously identified.

FROM THEORY INTO PRACTICE

There of course comes a stage when the designers/planners of any transportation system must give way to the ultimate operators. In the particular case of the Channel Tunnel project this will entail the transfer of knowledge from Transmanche-Link to Eurotunnel Operations Department (via ET's Project Implementation Division) in order that the actual procedures can be written prior to opening. Once prepared, all procedures are to be checked by TML in order to ensure that they are consistent with the design. The most important of these procedures will then be scrutinised by Eurotunnel's Safety Department, by the Maitre d'Oeuvre (independent project managers approved by the IGC) and the IGC/SA. The Concession Agreement specifies that Eurotunnel shall submit to the IGC for approval the operating rules for the Fixed Link which they propose be introduced.

CONCLUSIONS

The Channel Tunnel is a unique project both in terms of scale and concept. Eurotunnel and Transmanche-Link have accordingly been presented with a simultaneous problem and opportunity. The problem is that the nature of the enterprise precludes any possibility of importing procedures from other transportation systems for dealing with emergency incidents. The opportunity is to develop a methodology for the project, and apply it from design concept stage through to actual operations. This methodology is presented in summary form in Figure 4. It is believed, and this paper has attempted to demonstrate, that the methodology applied will make a major contribution to ensuring that all Eurotunnel staff have a pre-determined series of actions which they can undertake in the event of an emergency incident and which will provide valuable guidance at a time when such assistance is of enormous benefit.

The essence of emergency procedures is that they should be:

    easy to teach
    easy to comprehend
    easy to remember
    easy to apply
    easy to co-ordinate

The principal objective of the standard response is to meet these requirements.

We started this paper with a reference to the work of other railway administrations in preparing pre-determined plans for dealing with emergencies. Normally, the history of the development of these plans is that they are changed in response to failure in practice, or to changing circumstances. In so doing, the benefits of the application of an overall, comprehensive methodology are lost.

The authors believe that the sequence of steps outlined in this paper might be employed beneficially, not only by the sponsors of new transportation systems, but also by the operators of existing systems. The advantages of such an approach can be summarised as follows:

(a) the owners/operators of a system can be confident that all potential hazards have been identified;

(b) pre-conceived notions of safety can be re-examined;

(c) the interfaces between the different aspects of design and rail operations can be fully taken into account;

(d) operators can feel confident that their safety requirements have been taken into account in the design;

(e) the common strands of response in different incidents can be identified in order that these elements be combined in a standard response.

Overall, considerable benefit will have been achieved from a comprehensive and methodical reviwe of potential hazards. This process of analysis will not only ensure that the hazards are dealt with systematically, but will also provide the maximum assistance through simplified standard responses, to those staff charged with the responsibility for dealing with emergency incidents.

TABLE 2.3 | **DERAILMENT - EXCESSIVE SPEED**

Ref.	POTENTIAL RISK	PREVENTIVE MEASURES	CONSEQUENT HAZARDOUS EVENT	PROTECTIVE MEASURES
1A	ABNORMAL FUNCTIONING OF ATP SYSTEM	- A SEPARATE STUDY IS IN PROGRESS	- DAMAGE OR DESTRUCTION OF ROLLING STOCK EQUIPMENT - COLLISION WITH TUNNEL WALL AND DAMAGE OR DESTRUCTION OF TUNNEL EQUIPMENT - AFFECTED WAGON HAS TO BE ABANDONED - POSSIBLE PANIC POSSIBLE ESCALATION A MAJOR DERAILMENT COULD BE ACCOMPANIED BY FIRE, EXPLOSION, FLOODING, ABNORMAL DECELERATION AND LOSS OF TRACK. THE RESULTING EMERGENCY ACTIONS ARE COVERED IN THE EMERGENCY SITUATIONS ANALYSIS	- TUNNEL TRACK SUPPORT MAY PARTIALLY CONTAIN DERAILED WHEELS - TRACK IS FITTED WITH DERAILMENT DETECTORS - AUTOCOUPLERS ENABLE A 3-WAGON UNIT TO BE RAPIDLY DECOUPLED
1B	FAILURE OF ATP SYSTEM (CONTINUOUS SPEED CONTROL)	- ATP SYSTEM IS 'FAIL SAFE'	AS 1A	AS 1A
2		- MAINTENANCE TRAINING AND INSPECTION	AS 1A	AS 1A
3	MAINTENANCE ERROR RESULTING IN INADEQUATE BRAKING	- ATP ACTUATES EMERGENCY BRAKES (GSPEC)		

FIGURE 1: SPECIMEN PAGE FROM HAZARD ANALYSIS

GRS535

SCENARIO REF. No. 1
PART ONE - DESCRIPTION OF INITIAL SITUATION

MINOR DERAILMENT (1 WAGON) AT MIDPOINT OF TUNNEL

CONDITIONS ARISING

- EQUIPMENT CONSEQUENCES:
- CATENARY NOT DAMAGED
- COOLING CIRCUIT NOT DAMAGED
- BOGIE AND UNDERFRAME DAMAGED ON DERAILED WAGON
- ALL ON-BOARD SYSTEMS FULLY OPERATIVE - DECOUPLING POSSIBLE
- NO SIGN OF TRACK DAMAGE

- HUMAN CONSEQUENCES:

- KILLED - 0
- SERIOUSLY INJURED - 0
- SLIGHTLY INJURED - 1 - 3

PART TWO - ANALYSIS OF SCENARIO

SEE ATTACHED SHEETS

PART THREE - COMMENTS ARISING

A. AS THIS SCENARIO DEVELOPS, IT IS SUPPOSED THAT 3 TRAIN ATTENDANTS ARE ON THE SINGLE DECK RAKE AND THAT THEY WILL QUICKLY REACH THE INCIDENT SITE

B. IT IS CONSIDERED ESSENTIAL THAT THE REAR PORTION OF THE TRAIN PROCEEDS AT LOW SPEED (20 km/h) FOR A DISTANCE OF 5 km AS THE TRACK COULD HAVE BEEN DAMAGED BY THE DERAILED WAGON OR COULD HAVE CAUSED THE DERAILMENT.

DIAGRAMS

STUDY	
T.C.	TRAIN CAPTAIN
D.V.R.	DRIVER
R.C.C.	RAILWAY CENTRAL CONTROL
C.P.D.S	CROSS PASSAGE DOORS BETWEEN R.T.S. AND S.T.
C.P.D.N.	CROSS PASSAGE DOORS BETWEEN R.T.N. AND S.T.
R.T.N.	RUNNING TUNNEL NORTH
R.T.S.	RUNNING TUNNEL SOUTH
S.T.	SERVICE TUNNEL
C.P.	PASSENGER EVACUATION CROSS PASSAGE
P.R.D.	PRESSURE RELIEF DUCT
C.O.D.	CROSSOVER DOOR
T.I.	TRAIN NUMBER (SEE DIAGRAM)
N.V.S.	NORMAL VENTILATION SYSTEM
S.V.S.	SUPPLEMENTARY VENTILATION SYSTEM
S.T.T.S.	SERVICE TUNNEL VENTILATION SYSTEM
I.L.R.	1st LINE RESCUE
V.G.	CROSS PASSAGE DOOR VENTILATION GRILLS
EVACT	EVACUATION TRAIN
EMERT	EMERGENCY TRAIN
Q.A.	QUALIFIED ATTENDANT (EMERGENCY DRIVER)

FIGURE 2: SPECIMEN SUMMARY PAGE FROM EMERGENCY SITUATIONS ANALYSIS

GRSS01

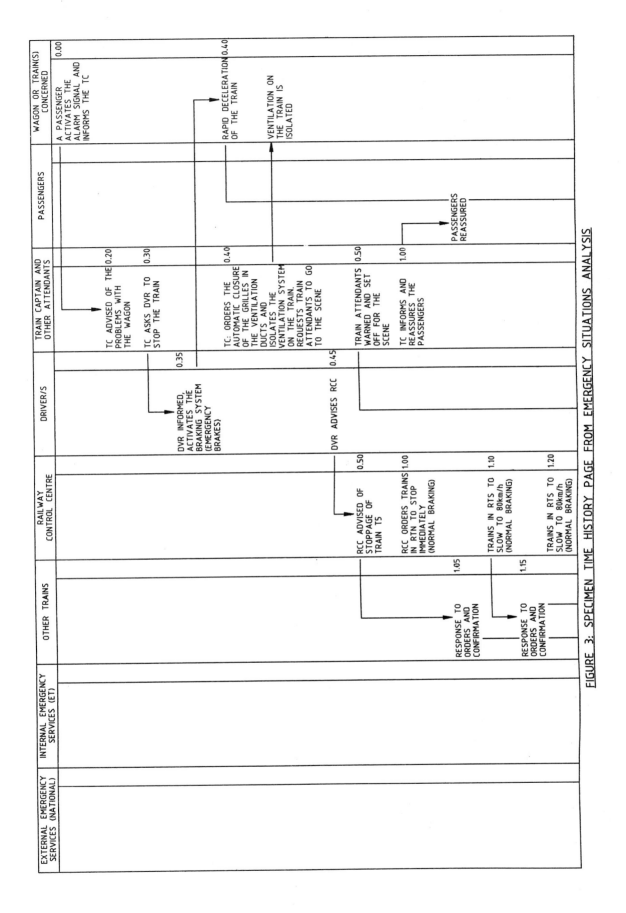

FIGURE 3: SPECIMEN TIME HISTORY PAGE FROM EMERGENCY SITUATIONS ANALYSIS

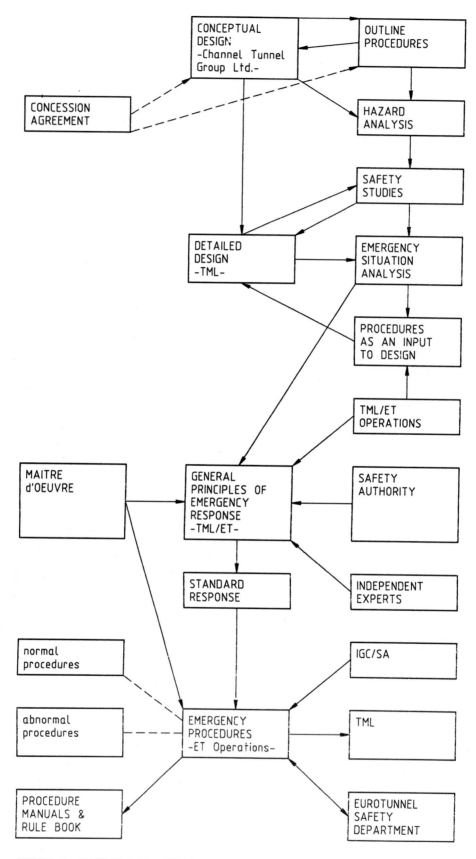

FIGURE 4: OVERVIEW OF METHODOLOGY FOR PRODUCING STANDARD RESPONSES AND OPERATING PROCEDURES

Safety on the Channel Tunnel high speed trains

A LAWTON, PhD, CEng, MIMechE
International Project Group, TGV-Transmanche, Paris, France

SYNOPSIS A description of safety measures that have been applied to the Cross Channel High Speed Trains, which will soon be running from Paris and Brussels to cities in the U.K.

1. INTRODUCTION

The title of this paper forms a question close to the heart of every engineer that has ever worked on these trains. It will also be a question posed by the majority of passengers at some time during their first trip through the Tunnel. This paper is the Railways response to that question.

The Channel Tunnel High Speed Trains (CTHSTs) will run from Paris and Brussels, through the Tunnel, to destinations within the U.K. The general layout of the trains, which are formed of two powercars and two, nine coach articulated half-trains, is shown in Fig. 1. The two half-trains together, provide an eighteen coach passenger train, which is about 400m long. Each train is capable of accommodating a total of 794 passengers. A fleet of thirty-one such trains has been ordered for the Paris and Brussels to London services; plus an additional seven which will be adapted to serve cities in the UK which are north of London, making a total of thirty-eight trainsets.

The technical emphasis of the trains is on a very high level of safety, security and reliability which is essential in view of the 300km/h maximum operating speed and the necessity to operate through the Channel Tunnel. For passengers, the emphasis is on providing a service which is able to exploit the inherent advantages of rail travel in terms of the amount of space available, the personal mobility which is possible and the comfort and general ambience which is achievable. All these are an essential part of the provision of a service quality which will lead to a profitable high speed train operation.

2. PASSENGER SAFETY PROVISIONS

2.1 PASSENGER ACCESS

All external doors will be closed and locked by the train crew, prior to departure. The door opening push buttons available to passengers will be inoperative, until the doors are unlocked by the driver on arrival at a station. In addition, an independent, supervisory system will provide secondary locking at speeds above 10 km/h.

Each external passenger door has an emergency release, available to passengers behind a lead sealed, transparent cover. Operation of this door release is signalled throughout the train by an alarm, broadcast over the public address system. Its use allows manual opening of a door at any speed, irrespective of locking action by the train crew. It will always be possible for passengers to open the external doors in case of an emergency. Also, it will be possible for individual doors to be opened, from outside the train, by emergency services.

The CTHSTs will operate over a variety of railway systems, with a large range of clearances between station platforms and vehicle door steps. This problem is particularly acute in the Tunnel, where a large "stepping" distance is necessary to accommodate the shuttle vehicles. The CTHSTs incorporate a pair of powered door steps, which adjust automatically to the correct configuration for each railway. If the step mechanism becomes disabled, the steps can be opened manually from outside the train. Failure of the steps to open correctly will inhibit the powered opening of the door. The emergency door release handle will allow door opening, regardless of the state of the steps.

Each door is designed for an emergency exit rate of 30 passengers per minute.

2.2 COMMUNICATIONS SYSTEMS

The communications hardware has been designed to have high reliability. Much of the hardware is duplicated. There are separate, independent systems which work in parallel to provide redundancy; the system is heavily protected against fire.

The public address and intercom systems share hardware such as amplifiers, telephone handsets, trainlines and interfaces to the electronic controller. The train alarm system will broadcast messages on the public address system and the train radio can be used through the intercom.

2.2.1 RADIO

The train crew have direct communication, via the train intercom and cab radio, with ground base. Incoming radio calls can be received at the driving cab and the train managers offices. Such calls will alert the train manager via the public address system, in case he is not in his office. Direct radio calls from ground base, via the public address system, to passengers are not possible, train crew will be responsible for all announcements to passengers.

2.2.2 PUBLIC ADDRESS

Train crew can make announcements to all passengers in the train, from the drivers cab, from the train managers office or from each coach vestibule. An override button is available at every public address handset in case of the need to interrupt an existing call in order to make an urgent announcement to passengers.

2.2.3 INTERCOM

An intercom system provides discreet communications between driver and other members of the train crew within the trailer cars. Intercom handsets are available in each driving cab, in the train manager's offices, immediately adjacent to the train splitting points and in each trailer car vestibule.

2.2.4 ALARM

An emergency alarm is available to passengers in each saloon. It alerts the driver and train manager in case of a problem with the train, but does not stop the train. A call for aid push-button is also available

beside each alarm which alerts the train manager, but not the driver. This button exists to minimise the utilisation of the passenger emergency alarm. No facility is provided for passengers to talk to the driver or train crew.

Various alarm or call signals can be broadcast over the public address system. In order of descending priority, these are :

· Fire alarm, to alert personnel responsible for fire fighting.

· Train manager alarm call, to indicate to the train manager, and driver, that the passenger emergency alarm has been operated, that an emergency, external door release handle has been operated, that the automatic fire extinguishing system has operated or that the "deadmans" alarm system in the driving cab has operated.

· Train manager call, to summon the train manager. Operation of this push button produces the same continuous tone over the public address as the alarm, but does not alert the driver.

All the above are supplemented by information on the nature and location of the alarm or call, which is displayed to train crew in the electrical cubicle of each passenger vehicle. These communications systems will continue to function for at least 90 minutes in the absence of the overhead line supply .

2.3 TRACTION SYSTEM

The traction system has been designed to minimise common mode failures which could immobilise the train. Traction systems at each end of the train are entirely independent. Within the traction system at each train end, there is a great deal of redundancy which allows considerable amounts of equipment to fail, without jeopardising the ability of the train to leave the Tunnel.

Continued running or restarting, even on the maximum Tunnel gradient, will be possible with only two motor bogies in operation, out of the normal six. (Each power car has two motor bogies and there is a third at the non-articulated end of the outer trailer car). A train entering the Tunnel with a power bogie out of service will be able to exit the Tunnel, even if one of the two power cars becomes a complete failure.

2.4 AUXILIARY SYSTEM

The auxiliary 500 V dc supply is produced by 4 separate units, 2 in each power car. Operation of

ny 3 of the units will provide all necessary auxiliary
power. Inverters, fed from the 500V supply, are used
power air conditioning cooling etc, and will be
similarly arranged so that failure of one unit will be
imperceptible to passengers.

PRECAUTIONS AGAINST FIRE

here are two principal precautions against fire,
hoice of materials and the ability to reconfigure the
ain.

.1 TRAIN RECONFIGURATION

he ability to reconfigure the train following a fire is
itally important. A CTHST can be configured as :-

- power car + 18 coaches + power car
  (normal configuration)

- power car + 18 coaches

- power car + 9 coaches

Within the train there are controls that will allow train
crew to split off a power car, if that power car were
on fire and had stopped the train, or to split the train
at the centre, if a fire within the passenger coaches
had stopped the train. These controls, which are
entirely manual, do not simply operate the
mechanical coupler, they reconfigure the train
computer system, control lines and braking system.
These controls change the train configuration
between the three states listed above so that the
effects of train damage can be neutralised and so
that a CTHST will, at least in part, always be able to
leave the tunnel.

3.2 CHOICE OF MATERIALS

The railways offered to their suppliers the choice of
using either of the two recognised standards, British
Standard BS 6853 or the AFNOR Standard NFF
16101, in the absence of an acceptable European
standard. This was on the understanding that the
standard adopted should be used for the interiors of
all the vehicles and all the rakes irrespective of their
country of origin, and that the part of the standard
relevant to underground trains should apply. The
suppliers chose to work to the French, AFNOR
standard.

The basic philosophy of the AFNOR standard is to
treat each different type of material and application
separately, and to specify an allowable fire spread
and smoke-fume performance. There is a
performance requirement for seat base foam, for
floor carpet, for ceiling carpet, for laminated wall

panels, etc. In each case, the requirement is
expressed in terms of a grid which shows which
combinations of fire-fume performance are
permissible and which are not. The standard relates
to materials which are actually available for railway
applications, and acknowledges that, for many
materials, various trade-offs are possible between
fire spread and fume performance by adjusting the
chemical composition.

4. TRAIN FUNCTIONING IN THE EVENT OF A FIRE IN THE TUNNEL

The philosophy is :

- Do not, deliberately, stop the train. Move
  passengers away from any fire and isolate
  them from the fire behind vehicle end fire
  doors.

- If fire forces the train to stop, try to restart
  the train.

- If the train cannot restart, evacuate as many
  passengers as possible to a part of the train
  that, by use of the splitting controls, will still
  be able to leave the Tunnel.

- Evacuate remaining passengers to the
  service tunnel.

4.1 FIRE AND A MOVING TRAIN

Objectives are

- Detect the fire as rapidly as possible

- Extinguish the fire, if possible

- Allow passengers the time to escape to
  other vehicles

- Contain the fire if it cannot be
  extinguished

- Maintain access to splitting controls

- Minimise passenger stress

Rapid detection of fire

The most likely source of fire on the train is in the
traction equipment. There will be an automatic fire
detection system within the major components of
electrical equipment in the power car and the motor
trailer traction compartment.

In the trailer vehicles, passengers will warn the train

crew via the passenger emergency alarm, which sounds a warning throughout the train, and gives an indication to train crew of the source of the alarm.

Extinguish fire

An automatic fire extinguishing system is installed in each power car and end trailer motor compartment. These systems can be triggered manually, using controls that are outside the traction equipment areas. The design and installation of these systems have been examined and approved by the Railways (of course!) and the design has been audited by an independent consultant for both reliability and for fitness for purpose.

An AFFF fire extinguisher of approximately 6 kg capacity will be carried in the vestibule of each trailer car (2 in vehicles adjacent to power cars), with an additional similar extinguisher in the baggage compartments and in the kitchen area of both restaurant vehicles.

Allow passengers the time to escape to adjacent vehicles

The time which is available for passengers to escape from a vehicle which is on fire is largely a function of the general layout of the vehicle itself, and of the properties, and particularly the fume opacity and toxicity, of the materials used in the train interior. The materials used have therefore been carefully chosen in order to minimise the possibility of passengers being trapped during the **early stages** of a fire.

Contain fire

To contain a fire which is incapable of being extinguished, the extreme end of each trailer vehicle will incorporate a partition and a door which have been designed and tested to give 30 minute fire resistance, according to the principles of the ISO834 standard. The railways have decided to use the fire doors as gangway doors which are normally closed in the Tunnel. However, they will be motorised to ensure that they are immediately openable from either side by passengers moving along the train or seeking to escape from the immediate vicinity of a fire.

Each passenger vehicle will have a floor construction which gives a half hour resistance to the spread of an under floor fire into the passenger compartment. The danger in the under floor area arises from potential electrical problems with the batteries and air conditioning heater banks. Special precautions will be taken to detect excessive currents or

temperature rises in this equipment. Brake pipes will be as far as possible from potential fire sources, brake equipment is isolated from any potential fire and protected against the effects of fire.

Maintain access to uncoupling controls

The vehicle end fire barriers will minimise the possibility that the area around the uncoupling devices will be either too hot or too smoke affected to allow train splitting to take place, if the train is subsequently brought to a stand.

Minimise passenger stress

In order to minimise the penetration of smoke and fumes from the exterior into the passenger areas from a fire on board the train, the driver may switch the air conditioning system to a full recirculation mode, and close the fresh air intakes on all the vehicles. This will also occur automatically if a power car or motor trailer car fire fighting system operates. This feature will minimise smoke and fume entry whilst at the same time allowing the cooling function of the air conditioning system to continue.

If there is a loss of the 25kV train supply, reduced intensity lighting will be maintained in all passenger vehicles for at least 90 minutes.

4.2 FIRE AND A STATIONARY TRAIN

Objectives are :

- To restart the train, if this is possible

- Allow passengers to transfer to the healthy half-train.

- Ensure reliable train splitting.

- Allow passengers to escape from the damaged half-train.

To restart the train

Within the R9/10 splitting equipment cubicle, is a control that will isolate the electrical system of the damaged half-train from that of the undamaged half-train. Therefore, if the train has stopped as a consequence of fire damage to a half-train electrical system, the fault can be isolated and the train will be able to restart. In effect, the undamaged half-train will drag the damaged half-train as though it were a set of air braked freight vehicles. After the electrical isolation, the damaged half-train may have a reduced level of passenger facilities. However, this will be a function of the precise nature of the damage at has been sustained.

Allow passengers to transfer to the healthy half-train

Unless the fire is immediately adjacent to the centre of the train, some passengers will be able to transfer to the other half-train. The width of the through passageway is 640 mm minimum at the saloon/vestibule doors and at other narrow points such as when passing the baggage compartment door mechanism. Aisle widths in saloons are 450 mm in standard class and 550 mm in first class.

Ensure reliable train splitting

The controls for reconfiguring the electrical and braking circuitry use mechanical linkages for resistance to heat, and are independent of all electrical requirements. The release of the couplers must be possible with high longitudinal forces locked in, as it is impossible to guarantee that the train will come to a stand in an emergency stop situation with a "slack" coupler. The required capacity (uncoupling with a 20 ton longitudinal force) is beyond the capacity of a simple manual lever system. The uncoupling will thus be done hydraulically by means of a manual pump powered by the person doing the uncoupling. At each uncoupling location, the necessary operation can be carried out from either of the two vehicles requiring to be uncoupled.

Allow passengers to escape from the damaged half-train

Given the many precautions taken by the Railways, the chances of an accidental fire stopping the train, with an uncontrolled fire on board, are considered to be extremely low. Nevertheless, there is always the possibility that this could be achieved by malevolent action. In this case, the train would stop at a point not under the control of the train crew and there would almost inevitably be some passengers between the fire and a power car who could not move along the train to the undamaged half and who would therefore need to be evacuated to the service tunnel. This could involve a walk along the Tunnel platform of up to 350m if a burning vehicle was badly positioned with respect to the nearest service tunnel entrance and the fire was too intense for passengers to walk past it along the Tunnel walkway.

To provide for this very serious situation, the train has been designed to shelter passengers by providing lighting, communication with train crew, protection against the spread of train fire and the ingress of smoke and fumes. Because of these precautions, passengers will be able to stay inside the train until the Tunnel ventilation system has, if necessary, been able to reverse the air flow direction to provide a flow of clean air between the train and Tunnel exit doors.

5. CONCLUSION

The railways have presented the specification design details and the physical reality of their trains to the Inter-Governmental Safety Commission (IGSC). The Railways have scrupulously followed IGSC guidance in all matters relating to safety. They are therefore confident that these trains, whether in the Tunnel or not, will maintain the traditionally high safety standards of BR, SNCB and SNCF.

ACKNOWLEDGEMENT

The author is grateful to the Project Manager of the International Project Group for permission to publish this document.

TGV TRANSMANCHE - 794 PLACES

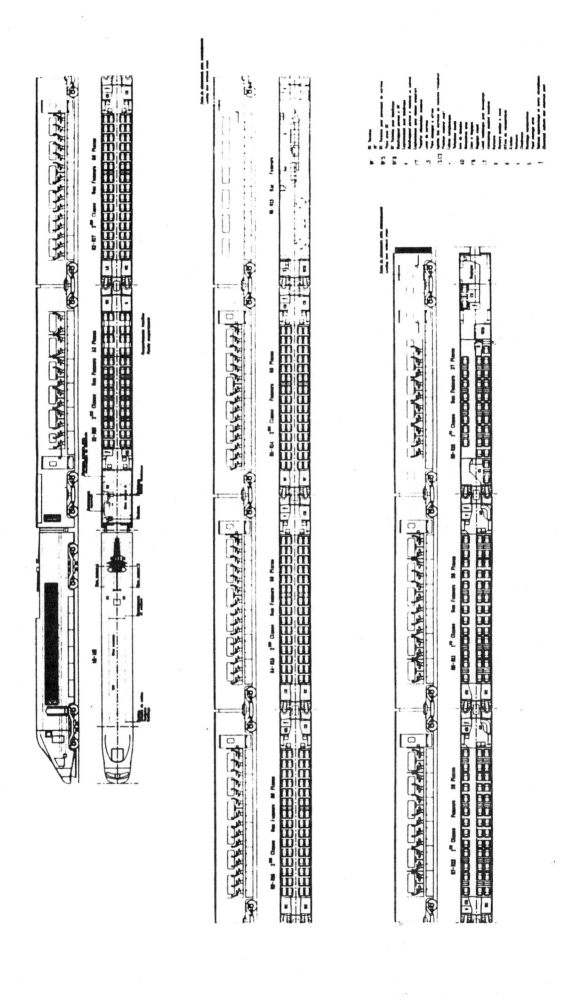

Eurotunnel rolling stock maintenance

P J RANDALL, MA, CEng, MIMechE
Eurotunnel, London

SYNOPSIS The fixed link will provide a railway shuttle service to carry almost all types of road vehicles between Folkestone and Calais. The rolling stock for this is not only technically complex due to safety requirements, but will be required to operate a mass transit type frequency of service, with a heavy rail system, in a harsh environment. This paper examines how the maintenance of this stock is being planned.

1   THE EUROTUNNEL FLEET

When the tunnel opens, half the capacity will be reserved for Eurotunnel's "Le Shuttle" service and the other part will be used by SNCF, BR and SNCB, the national rail networks for through freight and passenger services. These latter trains will be maintained away from the Eurotunnel system in the national networks' own specialist facilities. Eurotunnel will operate its own fleet of rolling stock to provide a roll on, roll off service from each country for virtually all types of road vehicle. To provide this service, various types of rail vehicle are being built under four main contracts but will be formed into two principle types of shuttle. One, designated the Tourist shuttle, will carry cars, caravans, trailers and coaches, together with their passengers who will, in most cases, remain with their vehicles. The second type will carry HGV lorries, and have separate accommodation, in a conventional railway carriage at the front of the train, for their drivers.

1.1   The Tourist Shuttle

The tourist shuttle will consist of 30 units in total, divided into two rakes. Each rake will have a loading wagon at each end and 12 carriers in between. Normally the leading rake will be single deck and the trailing one double deck, with the shuttle being completed with two locomotives, one at either end. Double deck carriers have capacity for 10 cars while the single deck can carry a coach, 2 cars and caravans, or 5 cars for example. With both types of carrier the basic design is the same and wagons are semi-permanently coupled into groups of 3, which are called triplets. Within each triplet certain equipment, such as the electric converters, is shared to enable economies in weight and maintenance to be made. The systems are locally controlled by a RS485 network which in turn is commanded from the train network. All wagons are pressure sealed, air conditioned and fitted with sophisticated fire detection, suppression and extinction equipment.

1.2   The HGV shuttle

The HGV shuttle will consist of 35 units, 2 rakes of 14 carriers with a loader at each end. In addition to these wagons and the two locos, there is also an amenity coach between the leading locomotive and the first loader. Drivers of the lorries will travel in this carriage, segregated from their vehicles for weight reasons. This results in the HGV carriers being much simpler than the tourist equivalent, not requiring air conditioning, fire doors, pressure sealing or passenger services which are provided in the latter. Diagram 1 shows the formation of the shuttles and their principle characteristics.

1.3   Other rolling stock

In addition to the stock mentioned above we have ordered 5 diesel locos from Krupp Mak which will be used for service work and emergencies both in the terminals and the tunnels. To allow their operation in the tunnel, without polluting the atmosphere, a pair of diesels will only be allowed into the tunnel with a "scrubbing" wagon between them, which will reduce the exhaust pollutants to an acceptable level (3 of these have been ordered from Percevaux). For tunnel maintenance work it is intended to use a swap body system, with maintenance equipment and materials mounted and transported on ISO container frames which are easily transferable between common, standard wagon bases.

1.4   Shuttle operation and utilisation

The concession is operated on a 24 hours a day basis and with a minimum frequency of one departure every hour. The requirements on availability vary greatly, and are usually different at any time for the tourist and HGV shuttles. Eurotunnel does not intend to publish a timetable for use by the travelling public but provide a service based on traffic predictions, and retain the ability to adjust on a very short time scale if demands require. Although the total rolling stock fleet numbers over 500 units, the length of the trains is such that it will only be possible to form 9 tourist and 8 HGV shuttles; each of these trains therefore respectively represents 11 and 12% of the fleet. These combinations of factors result in a very demanding availability requirement for shuttles. In turn this meant a radical approach to maintenance philosophy was necessary so that the flexibility of service could be maintained while still achieving high rolling stock utilisation figures.

To achieve this the maintenance work is carefully and individually planned for each system on a vehicle to ensure that preventative work is done at the optimum frequency, corrective work is dealt with quickly and efficiently and to leave provision to progressively introduce conditional maintenance on certain components.

In summary, the principle objectives are to achieve maximum reliability and cost effectiveness with minimum downtime.

2   MAINTENANCE FACILITIES

2.1   Platform facilities

To achieve the high targets mentioned earlier, the maintenance facilities have been carefully designed to minimise downtime. However, there is an inevitable downtime which occurs when moving a train out of service and into a maintenance facility, no matter how close the depot is to the terminal. To ensure that we only take a set out of traffic when absolutely necessary and that this is managed efficiently, we must know, as accurately as possible, what is wrong, as soon as possible.

For this reason the first line of maintenance will be based on the two platform areas, in Folkestone and Calais. Teams of "Trouble Shooters" working from road vehicles will be available round the clock to diagnose faults. In conjunction with the Railway Control Centre and the Rolling Stock Co-ordinator (one of the Maintenance team Group Leaders) they will decide on the most efficient time and place to do the repairs. This may well be in the platform areas, but because of the amount of equipment mounted under the wagon floors and the low height of them this will be limited in some instances.

2.2   UK site - Cheriton

The UK terminal is, at 300 hectares, less than half the size of the French site (700 hectares). Geographic constraints sandwich it between the North Downs and Folkestone and have necessitated the decision to put the main rolling stock maintenance facilities on the French terminal. However, there will be some facilities on the English site, built as part of the

combined Fixed Equipment and Rolling Stock Maintenance building. This consists of two basic areas :

(a)   A small workshop of 750m² with a single single ended road 28m long, with a central pit and 4 x 35 tonne capacity jacks. This area will also be used for road vehicle maintenance. No catenary is provided in this shop.

(b)   A double ended shed, 115m long fitted with catenary and with access to and from the terminal loop lines at both ends. In this shed the tracks are pillar mounted 1 m above the sunken floor. Platforms are provided at strategic points to access the interior of vehicles and there is also a roof height platform provided, to which access is controlled by interlocking with the catenary supply.

It is intended that these facilities are used mainly for emergency repairs, where transit to the main workshop would be either too time consuming or impractical. There is also a small amount of preventative work planned - such as diesel loco maintenance. Diagram 2 shows a plan of the English buildings.

2.3   The French site - Coquelles

As mentioned earlier, the major facilities for rolling stock maintenance are all based on the French site, because of geographic constraints on the English site. The main facility is a single, 10,000m² building divided into two main areas separated by the stores, offices and machine tools which are within the main structure. The use of the two halves can best be understood by first looking at the principles of preventative maintenance. These are fully explained later but in general can be summarised as follows. Each week, every shuttle is stopped and split into its two constituent rakes. These then pass through the "servicing" area to receive a safety inspection, a proportion of the annual preventative maintenance work and any outstanding repairs. This work is planned to ensure that a constant workload and downtime is achieved. Only if a job cannot be done in the downtime of a rake or if it requires equipment not available in the servicing area will a vehicle be taken out of its rake and put in the "workshop" area for these repairs to be done. The actual facilities in each area, are as follows :

2.3.1   Servicing area : There are 4 tracks in the area, each mounted 1m above the sunken floor, with a length of 92m. The actual distance between the doors is 115m, the difference being taken up by the bogie drop which allows bogies to be removed from the underside of any of the carrier wagons and exchanged with ones repaired in the workshop. Outside each road there is about 400m of track on each side of the shed, allowing rakes to move progressively through

© IMechE 1992 C451/031

the shed and be inspected and maintained. All the roads have catenary fitted, allowing the locomotive on the rake to power it through the shed for maintenance. Between each pair of tracks there is a platform to allow access to the vehicle interiors. An important feature is the easy access to all areas by fork lifts or maintenance vehicles. To achieve this ramps are provided from a subway under all roads to the depressed floor and the platforms making the movement of heavy equipment very much easier. Roof height access is again provided, on all 4 tracks, interlocked with the catenary supply to prevent access while the catenary is energised. This allows the locomotive to be maintained as an integral part of the train. The width of the carrier vehicles makes access to some of the underslung equipment very awkward. To facilitate the exchange of these components, sections of rail on 3 of the 4 roads are hinged horizontally to improve access. The fourth road is fitted with the wheel-lathe which is thus able to reprofile wheels on rakes which are on scheduled maintenance without the need to transfer to another track. The pit for the wheel lathe is provided with the space to install a second lathe at a future date. This will be important in reducing downtime for scheduled reprofiling and corrective work on our locomotives, where both wheelsets on a bogie need to be the same size because of the asynchronous drive configuration.

2.3.2 **Workshop area** : The four roads in this area are all single end access, and without catenary. One road has a depressed floor, pillar mounted tracks and platform for vehicle access. This is designed to allow repairs to systems where equipment is mounted beneath the wagons while their controls are fitted to the interior. The other three roads are fitted with flat floors at rail head level and central pits. All are served by a 250 kN overhead crane, and one has a synchronised set of 12 x 17.5 tonne jacks which will allow all 3 vehicles of a tourist triplet to be lifted without uncoupling. One of the other roads is constructed to take the 4 x 35 tonne jacks which will lift the electric locomotive. To enable bogie changes and repairs to be carried out, a series of 4m diameter turntables connect the bogie drop with the workshop, a cleaning booth and a repair track served by a 100 kN overhead crane. There is also an area equipped with a lathe, milling machine, surface grinder and turret drills. Diagrams 3 and 4 show a plan and cross section of the maintenance building in France.

2.4 **Subcontracting policy**

There are, of course, many facilities which it is uneconomic to purchase. This is either because the initial cost could never be justified - as with a press to remove wheels from axles,for example, or because the low utilisation means that it is impossible to keep staff competence and experience at a good level. To cover this work, which will be mainly in component repair and overhaul, contracts with specialised companies will be let to allow effective partnerships to be developed.

3 **CORRECTIVE MAINTENANCE**

Our maintenance policy is based around an efficient preventative maintenance programme which should minimise breakdowns in service, however these will inevitably occur. To deal with these as effectively as possible, specialist teams of trouble-shooters will be provided on each platform area. These will provide 24 hour cover, 7 days a week. The number of staff in each team will vary according to the intensity of service, but will usually be 2 at each terminal at any time.

3.1 **Organisation**

Any faults occurring in service will be reported by the train crew directly to the rolling stock co-ordinator or the rail control centre depending on the severity of the fault. This will allow vital time to plan the response that the team will make. A number of options are available to the trouble shooting team and it is their responsibility to choose a response based on the severity of the failure, and traffic conditions in conjunction with control. However, their first job will be to meet the shuttle on arrival to assess the problem accurately. The options are as follows:

(i) Repair immediately in platform area
(ii) Allow to continue in service, deferring the work to a later date, to be done either after a later trip or on the next scheduled maintenance
(iii) Take the shuttle out of service, to be repaired either in platforms, emergency facilities or the main workshop.

Their decision will primarily be concerned with the safety implications but also take into account effects on availability, reliability and traffic constraints.

3.2 **Work content : trouble-shooting**

The trouble-shooters will be mobile and equipped with tools and stores to do all normal running repairs and some specialist test equipment. Their high level training will allow a fast accurate assessment of problems to be made, and where possible immediate repair. Problems with electronics and control systems are envisaged as being most likely. The spares carried will concentrate on quickly replaced cards and modules and any vulnerable items which experience will no doubt identify. The main stores will be held at Coquelles but a trouble-shooting sub-store will be held in Folkestone.

3.3 **Work content : repairs**

If the fault on a train cannot be repaired because the facilities available in the platform area prevent it, the train will need to be transferred to either of the workshops. If it is both safe and practicable the train will remain in service and the work will be scheduled as soon as resources can be made available. If not, it will be taken out of service. The place of repair will be chosen, depending on the work required and resources available.

All repairs to major equipment will be effected by component exchange - followed by either repair on site (for small repairs, or sub-system exchange) or by sending module to sub-contractor.

For example if an HVAC (heating, ventilation and air conditioning) module fails and it cannot be repaired in situ, it will be exchanged in the servicing shed, using the bogie drop. If the fault can then be isolated to a sub- component, e.g. the compressor, this will be changed and the compressor sent away for repair. If the unit as a whole is faulty or damaged, the complete module will go for repair.

3.4 Major breakdowns

Should particularly severe problems occur, an on-call team is available to assist the trouble-shooting team. A senior technician will be available to assist with technical problems while a manager, a group leader and 4 technicians will also be on-call to deal with any incidents.

Normally if a train is unable to complete its journey, it will be assisted out of the tunnel by other trains. The procedures for this will be effected by the control centre and the trouble-shooters will intervene once the shuttle has arrived at a terminal. Should a train be unable to be assisted the on-call team with special equipment will be despatched to rescue it.

4 PREVENTATIVE MAINTENANCE

In general the minimum periodicity of preventative maintenance of railway vehicles is mainly dictated by safety inspections of running gear. For locomotives, this varies between 6 and 37 days, depending on service speed and the intensity of use, for coaching stock, it is usually about 10,000 km.

In our case, despite a relatively low speed of 130-140 kmh we have chosen 7 days which represents about 5,000 km in service to take account of:

- intensive utilisation (estimated to be 200,000 km/year)

- high load factors (22 or 22.5 tons per axle)

- the fact that our running gear is unique so past experience is not available.

Other equipment in general does not need inspection more frequently than every 1 or 2 months.

4.1 Organisation

Every rake, with its loco attached will pass through the servicing area every 7 days. The track on which the wheel lathe is located, can be used occasionally for this work as well, although it will normally be reserved for reprofiling. The downtime is expected to be:

8 hours for tourist rakes
6 hours for HGV rakes (subject to amendment following vehicle modifications)

As outlined previously we will plan individual examinations in detail. The co-ordination of routine inspections of running gear and pantographs with preventative maintenance of equipment and planned component exchange will achieve similar downtime and workload for each exam while allowing:

- individual inspection frequencies for different systems

- consistent workload for all groups of staff

- co-ordination of isolations for staff to work safely on equipment without delaying other work.

To achieve this a computerised information management system is being used (MMS - Maintenance Management System). This will maintain records of all modules and major components on each vehicle, their maintenance requirements and history and details of all unscheduled work undertaken. This information is used to build up the exam workload for each shuttle each week.

Repairs or component exchanges found necessary during inspection will be either:

- Done immediately if it will not affect other work being done

- Deferred, if it would hold up other work - provided it will not prejudice the vehicles' operation, affect safety, or reliability before the next scheduled examination

If neither of these options is practical then exceptionally the repair can be completed by replacing the vehicle or extending the downtime. This option is to be avoided whenever possible. Table 1 summarises the maintenance philosophy on the vehicle.

4.2 Work content : locomotives

As previously mentioned, the electric locomotive will be maintained as an integral part of the rake in the servicing area. Normal preventative work can be summarised as follows :

Below Solebar

- Inspect all the running gear, bogies and equipment cases.

- Replace parts such as brake pads, brake cylinders, and dampers.

- Carry out other repairs on electric, pneumatic or mechanical equipment.

Above Solebar

- Inspect roof mounted equipment, principally the pantograph.

- Replace pantograph heads, pantographs and other roof mounted equipment or that which is accessible through the roof hatch.

- Inspect all the internal equipment and replace as necessary those whose size and weight permits.

Other Work

Changing equipment that requires lifting the body (bogies, wheelsets, suspension...) or taking the roof off (transformer, equipment cases...) requires the loco to be moved to track 4 in the workshop. This track is equipped with a pit, jacks and a 250 kN overhead crane. (see appendices 2 and 3).

4.3   Work content : wagons

The installations in the Servicing Shed will enable nearly all day-to-day work to be carried out there.

4.3.1 Below Solebar The work described for the locomotives is effectively the same for wagons. However, in addition, the Bogie Drop, retracting track sections and tools such as lifting tables allow modules to be exchanged : wheelsets, bogies, air conditioning units, fire fighting modules, ventilation units...

4.3.2 Above Solebar Platforms situated at wagon floor level allow access to the interior of the rakes and enable loading and unloading via the loader vehicles, of large or heavy modules, tools or specially equipped vehicles. Only work on the couplings, gangways and bridgeplates needs to be done in the workshop, requiring that the vehicles be taken out of the rake concerned. Work on the roof of the wagons will be extremely rare and each will be dealt with individually.

5   PREVENTATIVE 'HEAVY' MAINTENANCE (OVERHAUL)

Modern Rolling Stock, built after the mid 70's does not need to be stopped and stripped down regularly for overhaul. The principle factors in this evolution are:

- Improved materials used for the body shells give increased corrosion resistance and better mounting of equipment.

- Better methods of surface preparation, priming and painting mean that an approximate coating life of 10 to 12 years can be achieved.

- Better quality cables and better methods of routing lead to increased life.

- The modular concept of equipment mounting allows its exchange without making the vehicle unavailable for long periods.

- Refinement of management techniques in maintenance planning - mainly as a result of using computer systems.

These mean that with the exception of certain specific jobs on the body shell or on the interior fittings, it will not be necessary to stop our vehicles for overhaul. However, there are certain constraints which are impossible to predict before we gain service experience.

We cannot judge the exact effect upon the vehicles of the humid, saline atmosphere in which they will have to operate. We will have to regularly examine the body work and fittings to determine the exact requirements and frequencies that will be required.

For the locomotives and amenity coaches it may be more economic for the 8-10 year overhaul to be carried out by another private or national railway company who are equipped for such work.

The size of the wagons effectively means all work must be done on site. A study, incorporating the experience we will have gained, will be carried out to determine the facilities needed to overhaul the vehicles. It is recognised that existing facilities will need to be extended to encompass this work. Table 2 summarises the various jobs and their frequencies which will be required to be done at overhaul level.

6 SUMMARY

This philosophy will allow us to achieve the following advantages over other approaches to Rolling Stock Maintenance.

1. Traditional "Railway Maintenance" techniques have required trains to be stopped for periods of between two and seven days on a regular frequency of every one or two months. This is avoided - by distributing the work on to weekly stoppages of much shorter duration - enabling extra trains to be available during daily peak traffic demands.

2. By utilising 'component exchange' methods vehicle downtime for overhaul or repair is dramatically reduced, and can even be undertaken in some cases without taking the vehicle out of the rake.

3. Computer programming allows each major item to have its own exam frequency, triggered on mileage, time in service or calendar date as suits it best. This maximises the efficiency of planned maintenance. This technique also leaves open the possibility of progressive introduction of conditional maintenance based on pro-active monitoring systems. This dramatically reduces the total workload and eliminates compromises in maintenance frequencies between certain components.

4. Well equipped and highly trained teams on the platforms will ensure that only repairs requiring the specific facilities in the workshop will be transferred there thus minimising non-productive mileage and downtime.

These techniques enable very high availability to be expected at certain times of each day to meet maximum traffic demand. During the summer season this period of peak availability is extended by decreasing the long term maintenance element in the servicing exam, by scheduling it during - for example - 10 months September - June only.

The maintenance of this new and complex equipment in a demanding environment presents a unique challenge. Our solution should enable us to meet this challenge safely and effectively.

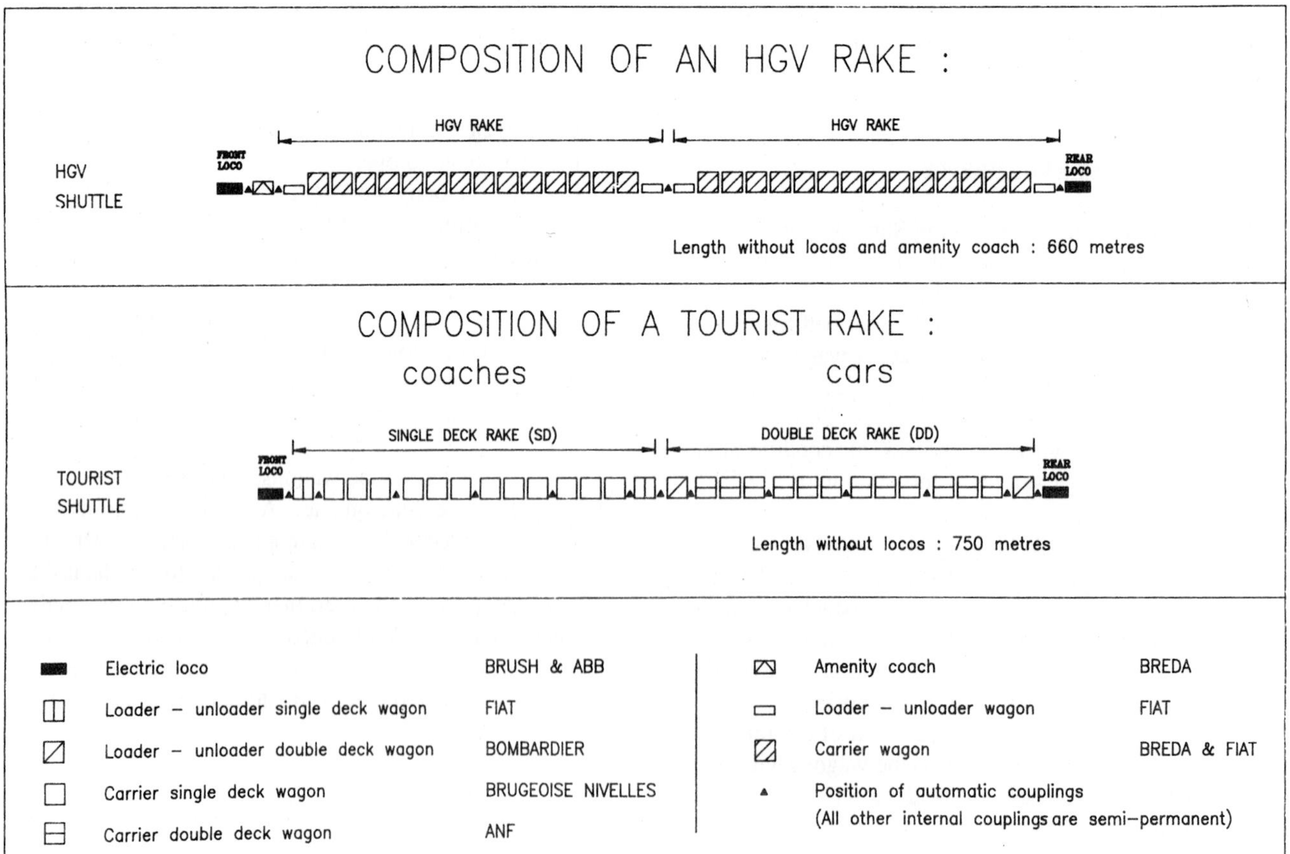

DIAGRAM 1

TABLE 1 - ROLLING STOCK MAINTENANCE DEFINITIONS

	DEFINITION	METHOD OF MAINTENANCE	METHOD OF REPAIR
SHUTTLE	The complete operational system that travels around the fixed equipment. It contains:- Locos, Loaders, Carriers and, a Passenger Coach in HGV shuttles	Split into rakes for maintenance	If not possible to repair in platform, in acceptable time, defective rake identified and changed.
RAKE	A self-contained proportion of a SHUTTLE, formed of Loading and Carrying VEHICLES, together with a Loco and in the front HGV RAKES, a Passenger Coach.	Will be maintained weekly in servicing workshop as defined in section 3	If not possible to repair in rake downtime, defective loco triplet or wagon taken out.
TRIPLET	A formation of 3 VEHICLES, either single or double deck carriers, that in general are never separated from each other.	Maintained in rake	
VEHICLE	A single self-contained item of Rolling Stock. It can be a Loco, Loader, Coach or Carrier etc	Maintained in rake	Repaired either in rake if time permits or taken out for individual repair
MODULE	A removeable package of assemblies that is fitted on a VEHICLE. A MODULE is repairable. It can be :- SERIALISED or NON-SERIALISED	Day to day maintenance : carried out on vehicle. Overhaul : module removed and sent to sub-contractors	If fault cannot be rectified in vehicle downtime, module or assembly will be exchanged. If module can be repaired by exchange of assemblies or parts this will be done, otherwise the complete unit will be sent to sub-contractors.
ASSEMBLY	A unit formed of PARTS to perform a specific function. May be part of a module. An ASSEMBLY is repairable. It can be :- SERIALISED or NON-SERIALISED	Day to day maintenance : carried out as part of module or in its own right on vehicle. Overhaul - Assembly removed and sent to sub-contractors	
PART	An item that may have its own function on a VEHICLE, or form part of a greater grouping than on its own. i:e: An ASSEMBLY or a MODULE. A PART can be :- REPAIRABLE - SERIALISED NON-SERIALISED or NON-REPAIRABLE (will always be NON-SERIALISED).	Day to day maintenance : carried out on vehicle Overhaul : if repairable removed as part of assembly/module, or on its own and then sent to sub-contractors	Repairable parts will in general be repaired by sub-contractors who have specialist knowledge and equipment.

TABLE 2 - OVERHAUL JOB FREQUENCY

VEHICLE	JOB	FREQUENCY
ELECTRIC LOCOMOTIVES	- Replacement of corroded bodywork - Complete external repaint - Repaint and refurbishment of cabs	8 to 10 years
TOURIST WAGONS	- Complete internal clean, including removing panels to deal with inaccessible areas (air conditionning and ventilation ducts) - Repainting and refurbishing interiors where necessary - Replace gangway bellows where necessary	5 years
	- Replacement of corrosion damage and repaint of areas if required (the majority of the body is stainless steel)	10 years
HGV WAGONS	Replacement of corrosion damage on the body and repaint. **Note** other operations may be necessary as a result of the enclosure modifications	8 to 10 years
AMENITY COACH	- Complete internal clean including removal of panels to gain access to air conditioning and ventilation ducts - Repaint and replacement of worn/soiled interior components	5 years
	- Replacement of corrosion damage - Complete repaint internal and external	8 - 10 years
DIESEL LOCOS	- Same operations as the electrics - However, the periodicity could turn out to be quite different because of the engines use on works trains, which may cause a more rapid deterioration than usual	8 - 10 years

UK ROLLING STOCK MAINTENANCE BUILDING

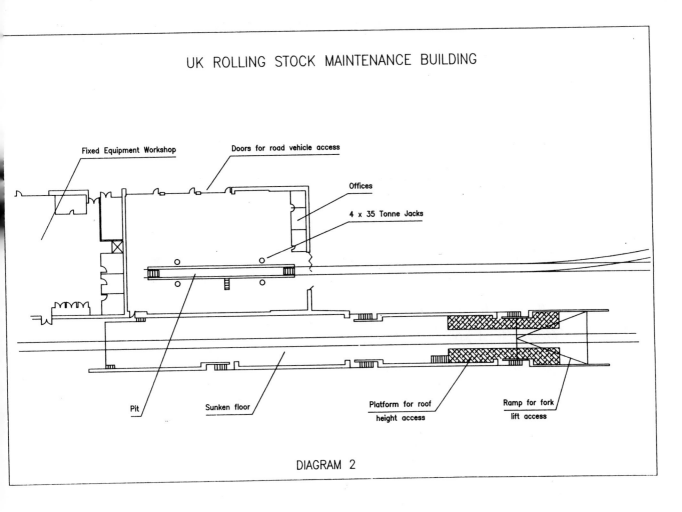

DIAGRAM 2

FRENCH ROLLING STOCK MAINTENANCE BUILDING

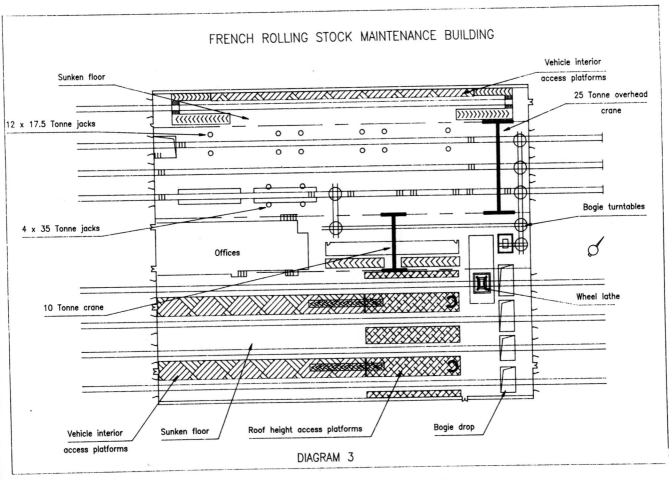

DIAGRAM 3

CROSS SECTION OF SERVICING WORKSHOP

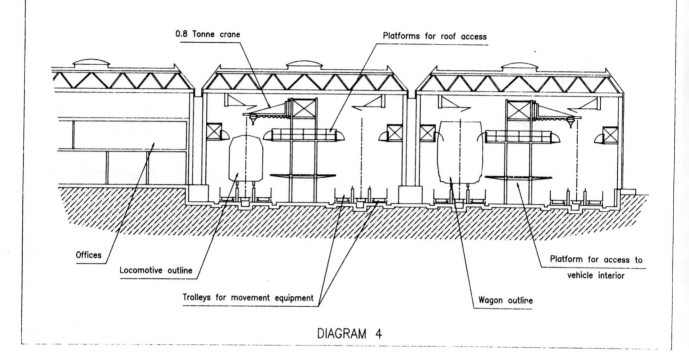

0.8 Tonne crane

Platforms for roof access

Offices

Locomotive outline

Trolleys for movement equipment

Platform for access to vehicle interior

Wagon outline

DIAGRAM 4

Automatic train protection system of the Seikan Tunnel for Shinkansen and other train operations

T TAKASHIGE, ME, MIEEJ, MIEICEJ and M NAOE, BE, MIEEJ
Railway Technical Research Institute, Tokyo, Japan
K KIMIZUKA, BE
Japanese Railway Construction Public Corporation Tokyo, Japan
M KADOWAKI, BE
Hokkaido Railway Company, Japan

SYNOPSIS   Signalling system of Seikan tunnel is described. Seikan tunnel is designed such that Shinkansen cars and other trains run on same track. Three-rail track circuit is developed to identify Shinkansen cars and other trains individually.

1   INTRODUCTION

Seikan tunnel is playing the role of main transport artery between Honshu and Hokkaido since opening in 1988. It is planned as the tunnel for both Shinkansen and non-Shinkansen trains (sleeping car, regional train and freight trains). Now, ordinary limited express is operated instead of Shinkansen. In Japan, the gage of Shinkansen differs from that of other lines. A three-rail track has been developed to enable Shinkansen and other trains to run on the same track in Seikan tunnel.

Seikan tunnel is 54km long. So, cab signal ATP (automatic train protection) system is adopted. ATP ground equipment are centralized on both sides of the tunnel. For trains running on different gages, a three-rail track circuit has been developed. This is a non-insulated track circuit using power frequency synchronized audio frequency. In the case of an undersea tunnel, a leakage conductance of track circuit is presumed to be very large due to a leakage of sea water. As maximum leakage of conductance is 3S/km according to a simulation test, track circuit is designed 250m long. ATP cab equipment adopts clock synchronous microcomputers system.

In this paper, signalling system of Seikan tunnel is described centering around ATP using a three-rail track circuit.

2   OUTLINE OF SEIKAN TUNNEL

2.1   Geographical position

Seikan tunnel is an undersea tunnel, linking Honshu and Hokkaido, about 600km north from Tokyo. Its construction work was started in 1971 with pilot tunnel holed through in 1983. Main tunnel was completed in 1985. Seikan tunnel was opened to service in 1988.

Fig. 1 shows an outline of the tunnel. Tunnel is 54km long. The undersea part is 24km long and underground part is 13km long at Honshu side and 17km long at Hokkaido side. Tsugaru channel separating Honshu from Hokkaido is 140m below sea level. The tunnel lies 100m below the bottom of the sea.

The undersea part is almost level with its gradient 3 per mil. Gradient of underground part is 12 per mil at both Honshu side and Hokkaido side.

2.2   Electrification

AC electrification in Japan always uses commercial frequency. Its voltage is 25kV for Shinkansen against 20kV for other lines. In Seikan tunnel, its voltage is planned to serve both Shinkansen and other trains. But, Shinkansen cars are not operated now, so its voltage is set at 20kV.

As telecommunication line runs through railway in Seikan tunnel, auto transformer method is adopted to decrease interference with telecommunication line.

2.3   Track

Track is unit slab bed. Rail weight is 60kg/m. Because variation of temperature is very small in the tunnel, super long rails are used except expansion joints at mouths of the tunnel and they are 53km long.

Railway in the tunnel is double track but approach line is single track.

2.4   Safety system

Seikan tunnel is very long, so safety systems nonexistent in other tunnels are provided; i.e. fire safety, earthquake alarm, drainage and ventilation.

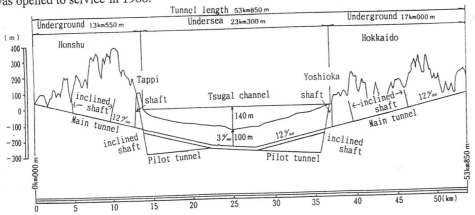

Fig. 1   Outline of Seikan tunnel

2.5 Signalling

Cab signal ATP is adopted and audio frequency non-insulated track circuits are used. Service brake for electric cars and emergency brake for locomotive are worked when the train speed is higher than its permissible value. Approach lines to tunnel adopt automatic block system with wayside signal. Both systems are automatically switched upon information received through track circuit.

3 THREE RAIL TRACK CIRCUIT

3.1 Necessity for three-rail track circuit

Gage of Shinkansen is different from that of other lines in Japan. The former is 1435mm and the latter is 1067mm. In Seikan tunnel, both trains run on same track, i.e. three-rail track. As shown in Fig. 2, one rail is common to Shinkansen and other trains and the other two are exclusive for Shinkansen and for other trains. Those rails are named c-rail, s-rail and o-rail in that order.

As Shinkansen cars do not run now, the two rails are intended for other trains. But, the three-rail track lacking s-rail is in place so that it will be easy to introduce Shinkansen in future.

Track circuit is designed as three-rail track circuit to identify individually Shinkansen cars and other trains and to detect all broken rails.

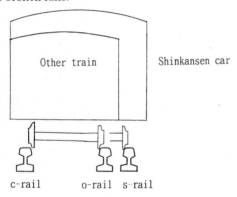

Fig. 2　Three-rail track

3.2 Conception of simulation

Rail that is transmission medium of track circuit is an electrically distributed constant circuit. Two-rail track circuit is analyzed by a four terminal constant circuit network. Three-rail track circuit needs to be analyzed by a multiple circuit network. Rails are directly connected to earth through rail/sleeper fastener. So, leakage current through earth is not negligible as leakage conductance between rail and earth is very large. In circuit analysis, earth is included as one of conductors. In the case of a three-rail track circuit, earth is the fourth conductor as shown in Fig. 3. Earth is a complete conductor with impedance zero.

Impedance and conductance per unit are as shown. Then, next basic equations are set up.

$$dV_i/dx = -\sum_{j=1}^{3} z_{ij} I_j \qquad (i=1-3)$$

$$dI_i/dx = -\sum_{j=1}^{3} y_{ii} V_i - \sum_{j=1}^{3} y_{ij}(V_i - V_j)$$

If x is a very small value, then dV_i/dx and dI_i/dx become as follows;

$$dV_i/dx = V_i - V_i' \qquad dI_i/dx = I_i - I_i'$$

In computer simulation, the above equations are computed by method of concentrated constant circuit network by dividing the section into small parts.

Self impedance of rail and mutual impedance between two rails are calculated by using Carson-Pollaczek's formulae. Leakage conductance between rail and earth is twice the leakage conductance between two rails. Shape of rail is complicated, so rail is equated to cylindrical conductor whose length of circumference equals to the length of rail surface.

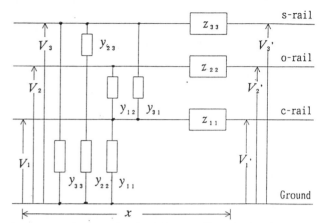

Fig. 3　Equivalent circuit of three-rail track circuit

3.3 Characteristic of three-rail track circuit

As a result of calculation about three-rail track circuit, the following are known;
(a) Transmission attenuation loss from transmitter to receiver in three-rail track circuit almost equals to that in two-rail track circuit.
(b) Train shunt sensibility of transmitting and receiving ends of three-rail track circuit almost equals to that of two-rail track circuit. But, train shunt sensibility of center of former is smaller than that of latter because signal current flows through another non-shunted rail by induction.
(c) If common rail (c-rail) is broken, rail-break is not detected because signal current flows through two individual rails (s-rail and o-rail).

Signal current in each case is shown in Fig. 4. We explain using ordinary track circuit. In absence of a train, signal current flows between o-rail and c-rail. In case of center shunt of track circuit by train axle, a loop current that flows between transmitter and shunt by axle induces to s-rail as indicated by (b). The induced current again induces to a loop circuit of ordinary rail at receiving end. Then, received voltage does not become so small as in case of shunt by transmitting and receiving ends. Received voltage by shunt of transmitting and receiving ends is smaller proportionally to shunt resistance. But, received voltage by shunt of center does not become smaller proportionally to shunt resistance in case of very small shunt resistance. Voltage becomes rather high on account of smaller shunt resistance.

In case of o-rail-broken, received voltage is more than 19dB smaller than normal level. But, in case of c-rail-broken, received voltage is about 6dB smaller than normal level because signal current flows through s-rail. Due to attenuation of 6dB, a broken rail is not detected. By calculation of current, current flowing through broken rail is very small and currents in s-rail and o-rail are equal in magnitude and opposite in direction. So, by measuring current difference between s-rail and o-rail, c-rail-broken is detected. Current difference is large in normal condition. If c-rail is broken, the difference in current becomes small. This change of current is same as change of received voltage when a train is detected.

The voltage at each point of track circuit by simulation almost equals to that of field test by three-rail track circuit as shown in Table 1.

© IMechE 1992 C451/022

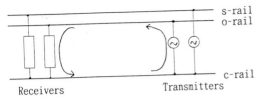

(a) Normal condition

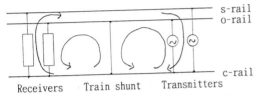

(b) Train shunted by the center

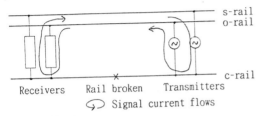

(c) C-rail broken

Fig. 4   Signal current flow in three-rail track circuit

Table 1   Comparison of calculation and field test of three-rail track circuit

		Voltage(V)			Current(A)		
		Ordinary line	Shinkansen	Between s-rail and o-rail	Ordinary line	Shinkansen	Between s-rail and o-rail
Transmitter end	Field test	7.28	2.69	4.84	0.92	0.99	-
	Calculation	7.21	2.86	4.63	0.81	1.17	0.5
Receiver end	Field test	2.3	0.53	-	0.6	0.74	-
	Calculation	2.33	0.88	2.72	0.67	0.92	0.39

3.4   Types of non-insulated track circuit

There are two types of non-insulated track circuit as follows;
(a) Shunted boundary --- shunting boundary of adjacent track circuits by resonated impedance.
(b) Multiple frequencies --- using multiple frequencies avoid malfunction of receiver by overreach from another track circuit.

The two types are outlined in Fig. 5. Former needs only two frequencies for train detection. In general, two carrier frequencies are alternately used for adjacent track circuits. Boundary of track circuits is very clearly detected. But, complicated resonated impedance consisting of inductance and capacitance must be provided for shunting and power is consumed by that impedance.

Latter needs several frequencies for train detection and boundary of track circuits is not clearly detected. But, circuit of boundary is very simple and power is consumed less than in former.

In case of cab signal, boundary of track circuits needs not be detected so clearly. So, we adopted multiple frequencies type. ATP signal is sent to a train for only the train detects track circuit. Transmission frequencies for ATP are differ-

ent from those for train detection.

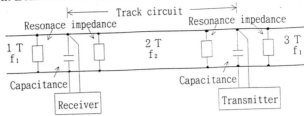

(a) Shunted boundary type

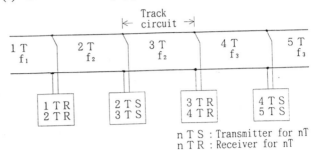

nTS : Transmitter for nT
nTR : Receiver for nT

(b) Multiple frequencies type

Fig. 5   Types of non-insulated track circuit

3.5   Maximum leakage conductance from rail to earth

In Kanmon tunnel between Honshu and Kyushu constructed before Seikan tunnel, sea water leaks much. We expected sea water leaks as much in Seikan tunnel, too. Maximum length of track circuit must be shortened if leakage conductance between two-rails becomes large by leakage of sea water to rail/sleeper fastener.

We must presume maximum leakage conductance of track circuit. Using same slab in Seikan tunnel, we measured leakage resistance between rail and earth. We laid 5m track circuit on that slab for test and measured resistance between two-rails under condition of sea water (3% salt water) being sprinkled 400mm above rail/sleeper fastener at a rate of 10mm/min. Then, minimum leakage resistance was 66ohm i.e. maximum leakage conductance was 3S/km. We designed the length of track circuit at undersea part of the tunnel by this value. On the other hand, at underground part, we considered maximum leakage conductance was same as that in mountain tunnel. Maximum leakage conductance for San'yo Shinkansen was 1S/km. So, we designed the length of track circuit at underground part for 1S/km.

3.6   Maximum length of track circuit

Receiver detects a train by a drop away at 14dB less than normal level. Pick up level is 12dB less than normal level. Then, we calculated the length of track circuit such that received level varies from 0S/km of leakage conductance to maximum, that is 10dB. Its length was 250m for 3S/km and 500m for 1S/km. So, in the tunnel, the length of track circuit is 250m at undersea part and 500m at underground part.

3.7   Electrical characteristic

Fig. 6 shows electric characteristic for three-rail track circuit. Track circuit length is 250m and measuring frequency is 1700Hz. Fig. 6(a) shows shunt resistance vs. attenuation level of receiver at center of track circuit. Attenuation level is lower as shunt resistance is lower. When shunt resistance is less than 0.1 ohm, attenuation level is not less than that value. By calculation, attenuation level is not less than the level due to 0.1 ohm of shunt resistance as shown in Fig. 6(b). Shunt resistance sensibility is more than 0.2 ohm.

Fig. 6(c) shows attenuation level of receiver vs. distance between receiving end and shunt point forward outside of track circuit. Shunt resistance is 0 ohm. Received level at no train condition varies as leakage conductance varies. Distance of train detection from receiving end varies from 5m to 45m before receiving end due to variation of leakage conductance. But, there is no problem in safety because it is not wayside signal but cab signal.

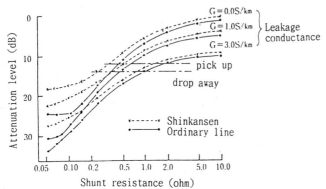

(a) Shunt resistance vs. attenuation level of receiver by field test (shunt in center)

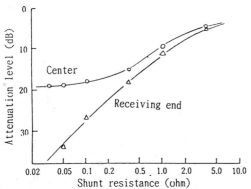

(b) Shunt resistance vs. attenuation level of receiver by calculation (shunt in center)

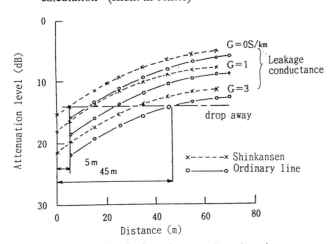

(c) Attenuation level of receiver vs. shunt location

Fig. 6 Characteristics of three-rail track circuit

Table 2 Characteristics of broken rail at receiving end

(unit:dB)

Receiver	Shikansen			Ordinary line			Broken rail detector		
Leakage conductance (S/km)	0	1	3	0	1	3	0	1	3
Broken rail s-rail	26.9	24.5	26.6	-0.4	3.5	8.6	-0.2	3.1	8.0
Broken rail o-rail	0.3	4.3	9.5	20.1	18.8	21.8	9.4	10.5	14.7
Broken rail c-rail	5.8	10.6	16.3	6.3	11.7	17.6	39.1	33.4	35.1

Table 2 shows variation of received level in case of a broken rail. The level is over 19dB lower than normal level in broken s- and o-rails. But, the level is only 6dB lower than normal level in case of c-rail broken. Received level for broken rail detection is 33dB lower than normal level.

4 ATP SYSTEM OF CAB SIGNAL

In Japan, ATP system on Shinkansen uses cab signal but signal system on most of ordinary lines does wayside signal. In Seikan tunnel, signal system adopts centralized cab signal for the following reasons;
(a) Shinkansen cars and other trains run on same track.
(b) Trains are stopped in emergency by ATP system when earthquake or train fire happens.
(c) Equipment are centralized on ground out of the tunnel for sake of easy maintenance.
(d) Driver may fail to recognize wayside signal in a fog caused by difference of temperature at mouth of the tunnel.

4.1 Constitution of transmitter and receiver for ATP and train detection

ATP and train detection transmitters are separated in multiple frequencies type non-insulated track circuit. Fig. 7 shows its constitution. Transmitter for train detection feeds two track circuits. ATP transmitter does the train detected by track circuit.

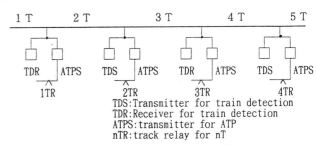

TDS:Transmitter for train detection
TDR:Receiver for train detection
ATPS:transmitter for ATP
nTR:track relay for nT

Fig. 7 Constitution of transmitter and receiver

4.2 Modulation

In three-rail track circuit, interference by traction current is larger than that in two-rail track circuit. For example, traction current flows through c-rail and s-rail for Shinkansen cars but does not through o-rail. Difference in voltage between c-rail and o-rail goes to receiver for ordinary line. This voltage is larger than that in two-rail track circuit. We adopt power frequency synchronized single side band (SSB) modulation type used for Shinkansen because it is strong against interference by harmonic of power frequency. Receiver operates stably for a noise current 30 times as large as signal current because the noise current frequency is only harmonics of power frequency.

4.3 Carrier and modulation frequencies

In power frequency synchronized SSB, carrier frequency varies as power frequency varies. Maximum variation of power frequency is 1%. So, carrier frequency is set below 2kHz because variation of carrier frequency is below 20Hz, then it easily locks harmonic of power frequency. For train detection, carrier frequencies are 1650Hz LSB (lower side band) and 1800Hz LSB for Shinkansen and 1550Hz USB (upper side band) and 1750Hz USB for ordinary line, and for ATP they are 1050Hz LSB and 1100Hz LSB for ordinary line and 900-1200Hz USB/LSB (compatible with that of Tohoku Shinkansen) for Shinkansen.
Modulation frequencies are 12, 16.5, 21, 27, 32, 38.5Hz both for ATP and train detection. For train detection, each of them is used in that order. For ATP of ordinary line, two out of them are combined. Number of ATP signals is

maximum 15 ($=_6C_2$). Now, 7 combinations are used.

4.4 ATP system

Operating principle of ATP is shown in Fig. 8. Length of one block section is about 1.5km. As length of one track circuit is 250-500m, one block consists of 3-6 track circuits.

Maximum speed of train is 140km/h for electric car, 110km/h for passenger train and 100km/h for freight train. Allowable speed of the train is a little different from that of the car. In case of passenger train, the following section of forward train is 'R0' whose allowable speed is 0km/h. The followings are '0', 'R45', '45', 'Y110' and '110' in this order. Their allowable speeds are 45km/h for '0' and 'R45' and maximum for others. Their signals are indicated by their alpha-numerics; 'R0', '0' and so on. Their colors are red for 'R0' and '0', yellow for 'R45' and white for others. If cab receiver does not receive any signal, cab signal indicates 'X' in red and the train stops. Driver acts according to the indication of cab signal. In normal operation, driver operates at less speed than allowable speed. If train speed exceeds allowable speed, emergency brake for locomotive works automatically. For electric car, service brake works. Service brake works when train speed exceeds allowable speed but it releases when the speed relation is reversed. Emergency brake once it works does not release until the train stops.

For high reliability and safety, ground equipment are composed of hot stand-by dual for transmitter and triple modular redundancy for receiver. Cab signal equipment consists of dual. Cab equipment use microcomputers but ground equipment do not. Clock synchronous microcomputer system is adopted for the sake of safety. By that system dual microcomputers are used and their bus data are compared at every clock.

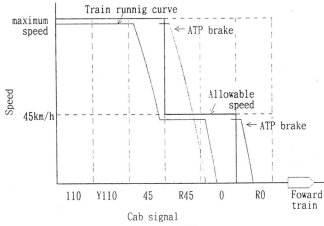

Fig. 8   Operating principle of ATP
(for locomotive)

5   DISASTER PREVENTION IN THE TUNNEL

5.1   Train fire

When a train catches fire, it does not stop in a tunnel or on a bridge but runs out of it and stops at safe point. As Seikan tunnel is so long, the train can not but stop in it. There are two stations provided for refuge and fire fighting at both sides of the channel. Passengers seek a refuge on ground through shaft.

There are eight fire alarms using infrared thermometer and five smoke detectors for train fire in the tunnel. Information on a fire detected gives an alarm at the instruction center of Hakodate. If a train fire is detected, train movement in the tunnel is safely controlled by ATP.

5.2   Earthquake

As earthquakes are frequent in Japan, earthquake warning is necessary. There are eight seismometers installed in the tunnel. They automatically sense the strength of earthquake, distortion of tunnel lining and change of water seepage and the train operation is controlled by ATP.

5.3   Drainage

Water seeps at a rate of about 18ton/min in the tunnel. In an undersea tunnel, water must be pumped out as the mouth of tunnel lies lower than its center. Water is drained through pilot tunnel. Drain pumps both sides of the channel are monitored and controlled from the center at Hakodate.

5.4   Ventilation

Heat caused by train running or waste gas from maintenance car is not dissipated sufficiently by natural ventilation but by ventilators. Fresh air is sent at a rate of 1m/s to center of the tunnel through the inclined shaft from both sides of the channel and ventilated through both mouths of tunnel. If the train stops at the refuge station in case of a train fire, heat or gas is eliminated by force through shaft to ground.

6   CONCLUSIONS

Ground equipment centralized on both sides of the tunnel and reserve ones are provided. The system has stably acted and has never failed since opening. ATC equipment are always monitored by a monitoring system. Monitoring items are voltage and current of each transmitter and receiver and relay operation according to train running. The information collected are displayed in the center.

Length of track circuit is designed for maximum conductance of 3S/km in undersea part and 1S/km in underground part. Water does not leak, so leakage conductance is very low in undersea part. But, in underground part, because the train scatters sand on slopes where top of rail gets wet in fog, rail/sleeper fasteners become wet and dirty. Then, leakage conductance is very large at that part. Now, rail/sleeper fasteners are periodically cleaned.

We described the signalling system in Seikan tunnel. We developed a three-rail track circuit because Shinkansen car and other trains run on same track. Now, only rails for other trains are being used. Trains run at maximum speed of 140km/h now but will do at 160km/h soon. In future, Shinkansen introduction is being considered.

REFERENCES

(1) Signal Engineering of Japan : "Seikan tunnel special", 1987 Vol.42 No.10 The Signal Association of Japan (in Japanese)

(2) Kitahara et al. : "Recent signalling technology of Japan National Railway", 1987 ditto (in Japanese)

(3) Takashige et al. : "Train detection characteristics of 3 or 4 rail track circuit", 1991 Vol.5 No.9 RTRI report (in Japanese)

C451/036

The Channel Tunnel signalling system

P M ROBINS, BSc, CEng, MIEE, MIRSE
W S Atkins and Partners, and Eurotunnel, Folkstone, Kent

SYNOPSIS: The Channel Tunnel represents a significant challenge for the Signal Engineer. The chosen signalling system must give a high capacity and at the same time must handle in complete safety a mix of trains. The selected solution is the TVM430 cab signalling system. This system makes use of audio frequency track circuits to transmit information from track to train. Processing both trackside and on train is carried out by the coded processor, originally developed for the SACEM system now operational in Paris. The paper describes the TVM430 system and how it is being applied to the Tunnel.

1. INTRODUCTION

This paper describes the signalling systems being installed in the tunnel currently under construction between the United Kingdom and France, under the English Channel.

The signalling system is responsible for maintaining the safe separation between trains and providing a means by which railway traffic is regulated. It is a requirement of the Concession under which Eurotunnel (ET) operates that a cab signalling system together with Automatic Train Protection (ATP) should be provided.

The signalling system has to be capable of handling in complete safety a mix of different train types: BR, SNCF and SNCB will jointly operate high speed trains between Paris, Brussels and London, running at up to 300 km/h outside the Tunnel, but restricted to 160 km/h within it. They will also run loco-hauled freight trains of various types at speeds from 100 to 140 km/h (and ultimately 160 km/h). The ET shuttle trains, which are 800 m long, will operate at a maximum speed of 140 km/h (again with an ultimate possibility of 160 km/h).

The performance target for the signalling system is a capacity of 20 train paths per hour in each direction, using shuttle braking characteristics but with a maximum speed of 160 km/h. This will be expanded in future to 24 paths per hour and ultimately 30 – though this latter target will require a different signalling system.

These paths are divided equally between the railways and ET. Since the performance of the railways trains is not the same as that of the ET shuttles, each train may require two or more shuttle paths. Thus in practice the likely initial maximum service is 15 trains per hour, 10 from ET and 5 from the railways.

This mix of traffic at different speeds and close headways, together with the stringent safety requirements imposed by the length o. the Tunnel, has lead to many special measures being taken in the Signalling and Control Systems.

2. THE SIGNALLING SYSTEM

A cab signalling system will be used; that is, all indications will normally be given to the train driver on a display in the driving cab. There will also be an Automatic Train Protection (ATP) system which will stop the train if the driver makes an error.

The cab signalling system selected is TVM430. This was developed by SNCF from TVM300, used first on the high speed line from Paris to Lyons. TVM430 will be used on the new line from Paris to the Tunnel (the TGV Nord), and its use within the Tunnel thus avoids the need to equip international trains with an additional set of on-board signalling equipment purely for use in the Tunnel. It also means that the driver has to be familiar with only four types of signalling (French, Belgian, UK lineside and TVM430), rather than five.

3. PHILOSOPHY

TVM430 will be implemented in the Tunnel using the same philosophy as on TGV Nord; that is, as a speed code system. The stopping distance is divided into four block sections in each of which the driver receives instructions to reduce speed. In addition there is an overlap block section, separating the stopping point from the occupied block section, and a warning block, in which the driver is alerted to the need to commence a speed reduction in the next block, (Figure 1).

The indication to the driver takes the form of a 3 digit, fail-safe display. If the line is clear and the train may run at full speed, this speed is displayed in black figures on a green ground. If the driver must slow down approaching a speed restriction or a preceding train, a target speed is shown, which is "000" in the case of a stop. This target speed is displayed in black figures on a white ground (red for a stop instruction). For permanent or temporary speed restrictions the speed is shown in white figures on a black ground. In the case of a speed reduction, if it must continue in the next block, the display will flash (Figure 2).

Because the display must be fail-safe the speeds displayed cannot be dependent on information entered by the driver. For the British Rail Class 92 locomotive, therefore, which has to haul trains with differing maximum speeds, no speed is given in the "line clear" aspect. A simple green indication is displayed.

The block sections are indicated to the driver by reflective signs known as "block markers". These provide an execution point for the instructions given by the cab display. If the signalling imposes a stop at a marker then it is said to be "closed", otherwise it is "open".

The driver is backed by an Automatic Train Protection system. If the train exceeds the maximum safe speed at any time by more than 10 km/h (5 km/h below 80 km/h), an emergency brake application is enforced to bring the train to a stand.

The signalling is of the absolute block type, as opposed to the permissive block working employed by SNCF on TGV and other lines. That is to say, a driver may not pass a closed marker without specific authority from the control centre. To enforce this, each marker is provided with a loop of cable between the rails which transmits a "stop" instruction to the train when the marker is closed. When verbal authorisation to pass the marker is received, the driver must operate a push button which overrides the effect of the loop for a limited distance.

After passing the closed marker and entering the overlap block section, an occupied block, or one where the ground equipment has failed, the cab display shows red and the ATP system limits speed to 30 km/h.

4. THE MONOPROCESSEUR CODÉ (CODED SINGLE PROCESSOR).

Both trackside and on-train equipment makes use of this device to carry out vital (ie. Safety-related) processing. A short description might therefore be appropriate at this point.

This device uses a single industry standard microprocessor (motorola 68000 series) to perform processing to a vital standard (probability of non detected error $< 10^{-8}$).

This is achieved by the coding and dating of variables and inputs. Each data item is represented both by its actual value and by a "signature" derived from the data and the number of the program cycle (the "date"). During compilation of the program a set of expected signatures is produced and this is stored in ROM. At run-time the signatures produced in real time are checked against these stored signatures. If an error is found the power supply to the outputs of the processor is cut, forcing them all to zero.

This mechanism protects against hardware faults, but not errors in the software. Software development and validation must therefore follow the stringent standards normally applied to the software for safety applications.

The Monoprocesseur codé was developed for use in the SACEM signalling system now in service on RER line A in Paris and has been validated and approved by the French Ministry of Transport.

5. TRACKSIDE EQUIPMENT

The TVM430 makes use of the running rails as the transmission medium. Audio frequency, jointless track circuits are used both for train detection and data transmission. Four carrier frequencies are available, two of which are used on each running line, alternating from track circuit to track circuit ie. f1,f2,f1 ... on line 1, f3,f4,f3 ... on line 2. This avoids problems with interference between track circuits on adjacent lines.

The carrier frequency is modulated with one or more from a total of 28 possible low modulation frequencies. One of these frequencies is used solely by the track circuit receiver to detect correct operation, leaving 27 available for data transmission to the train.

Any combination of these frequencies may be present at one time and the code transmitted from the track circuit may thus be thought of as a 27 bit digital word, the absence of any frequency representing a "0" in that bit position, the presence representing a "1". This word is divided up into fields, each of which represents an element of information required by the on-train equipment. These are speed code, gradient, block section length, network code, error checking.

The speed code represents in a combined form the current maximum safe speed for the train, the speed it should be doing at the end of the current block (the "target speed") and the target speed for the end of the next block. The code transmitted will depend, therefore, on the civil speed limit in force, and the state of track circuits ahead. The gradient is the average over the current block, the length of which is specified by the next field.

The network code allows the same track to train transmission system to be used on lines with different characteristics. Depending on the network code, the same speed code will be interpreted in different ways by the on board equipment. For example, on the high speed line the maximum speed is 300 km/h, requiring a particular interpretation of the speed codes. In the tunnel, where the speeds are much lower, a completely different interpretation is required. Thus the high speed line and Tunnel TVM430 systems will transmit different network codes.

The error checking field is a checksum of the previous fields, allowing the on-train equipment to verify correct reception of the codes.

Block section lengths in the tunnel will be around 450 m, considerably less in the terminals.

Track circuit transmitters and receivers are located with the processors which calculate the codes to be transmitted. These are housed in the Tunnel in equipment rooms at intervals of about 14 km, determined by the 7 km maximum feeding distance for the track circuits. There is thus no active equipment outside of the equipment rooms.

The codes to be transmitted are calculated by two non-vital processors and the results are compared by a vital processor, the "Monoprocesseur codé". If a discrepancy is found the outputs are forced to the safe state.

In addition to transmission by track circuit, a non-vital means of transmitting supplementary information, such as the stop instruction at closed markers, is available. This is a cable loop placed in the track where required, which transmits a phase-shift modulated digital signal. This is used in the Tunnel for several other functions including automatic control of loco power through neutral sections, automatic switching of the pantograph uplift stop and arming and disarming of the various on-train signalling systems.

All temporary and permanent speed limits are imposed through the TVM 430 system. Temporary restrictions may be imposed either locally, by switches located at each evacuation cross passage (every 375 m), or remotely, through the Rail Traffic Management system at the control centre. In the tunnel, speed limits of 100, 60 or 30 km/h are available. A 0 km/h speed limit may also be imposed as protection for engineering works.

6. INTERLOCKING

Interlocking functions are performed by standard SNCF PRCI (Poste à Relais à Commande Informatisée) equipment. All vital functions are performed by fail-safe relays, whilst non-vital control functions are performed by a series of dedicated microprocessors. This system has been described in the technical press (Institution of Railway Signal Engineers Proceedings 1986/87 - The New SNCF Electronic Interlocking at Tours), and will not be covered further here.

7. ON-TRAIN EQUIPMENT

The structure of this equipment is shown in Figure 3. The signal from the track circuit is detected by two pairs of antennas, one antenna from each pair over each running rail. These are mounted on the loco body, about a metre ahead of the leading axle. The signal from each pair of antennas is decoded by a digital signal processor, one per pair. The function of these processors is to demodulate the signal frequencies to produce the 27 bit data word.

The data is fed to a monoprocesseur codé forming the display processor, which performs the main decoding functions. If the data received from the two digital signal processors differs, the monoprocesseur signals an error, causing the system to shut down. This guards against hardware faults in the signal processors.

The display processor decodes the speed code field and drives the fail-safe cab display. The safety of the display is achieved by the use of a projection display, rather than one in which characters are generated by illumination of segments or dots. Each character to be displayed is printed onto a transparency and projected onto a screen by a lamp, one lamp per character. Each set of three lamps for a particular indication is illuminated by a relay, the state of which is read back by the processor. Energisation of the appropriate relay assures display of the required indication.

The display processer also passes the speed, together with the gradient and block length information to a separate processor which carries out the ATP functions. This processor uses this data to calculate a deceleration curve which the train should follow. The real speed is continuously monitored against this curve, and the emergency brakes are called if the safe speed is exceeded.

The real train speed is obtained from a fail-safe tachometer, which obtains three readings from two independently driven axles. These readings are processed separately, using diverse technologies and the results compared by a two-out-of-three voter. The processors have inputs from the braking and slip/slide protection systems and uses these to produce a speed measurement accurate to better than +/- 2%.

The ATP processor is not a monoprocesseur codé, but guards against hardware error by a different mechanism. Each program cycle is executed twice, using different memory areas and driving separate outputs. A hardware self-test routine is also executed every program cycle. Each output drives a separate relay, whose contacts are monitored by the processor. Contacts of these relays are in the emergency brake circuit, such that if either drops, the brakes are applied.

All on board equipment is monitored by a fail safe monitoring device, which cuts the power supply if a fault is detected. The on board system is completely duplicated for availability, so an emergency brake application is not made unless both equipments fail. This is because it is highly undesirable for safety reasons to stop trains unnecessarily in the tunnel, and this duplication minimises emergency stops caused solely by equipment failure.

8. CONCLUSION

The testing of the TVM430 system by the SNCF is proceeding satisfactorily, and the first installations on the TGV Nord line have been successfully commissioned. Installation of the signalling is now well advanced at the Terminals and in the Tunnel. All the indications are that the Channel Tunnel Signalling system will be ready to meet the challenge of ensuring the safety of the travelling public when this important project is put into service.

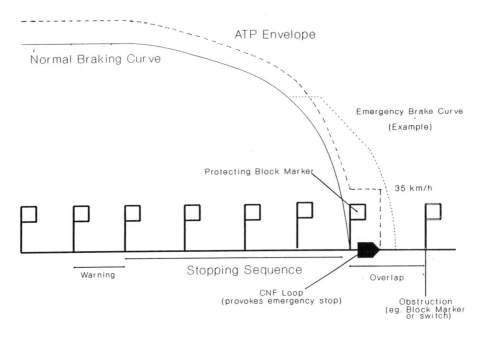

Figure 1. TVM 430 Principle

			Stopping Distance				Overlap
Shuttle	140	140	(140)	(115)	(80)	000	RRR
TMST	160	(160)	80	80	(80)	000	RRR
Locos	GGG	(GGG)	50	50	(50)	000	RRR

GGG = Green
RRR = Red
(---) = Flashing

Figure 2. Cab Displays

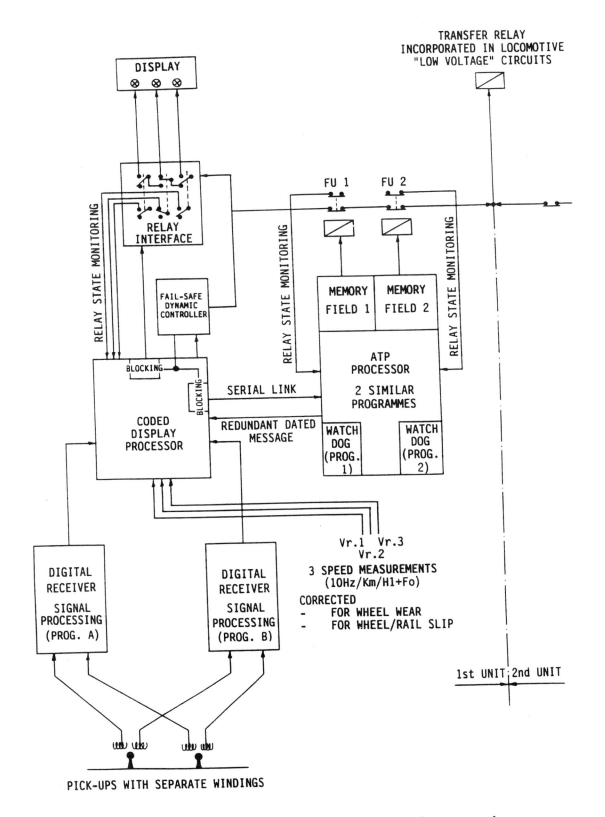

Figure 3. On-Train Equipment

C451/026

High-speed trains for the Channel Tunnel

R J KEMP, BSc, CEng, FIMechE, FIEE
GEC Alsthom, Paris, France

SYNOPSIS

Thirty-eight high speed trains are being constructed for services between the UK and mainland Europe. 31 of these will provide the "3-Capitals" services between London and Paris or Brussels. The remaining 7 will provide services between major cities North of London and Paris or Brussels. This paper describes the trains and the international industrial structure that has been created to build them.

THE TMST CONSORTIUM

In 1988 the three railways, BR, SNCF and SNCB, formed an International Project Group (IPG) to co-ordinate the procurement of trains for the Tunnel. It became clear that, for political reasons, contractors for the trains would have to involve the industries of all three countries.

A group was formed in 1987 under the name TMSTG (Trans-Manche Super Train Group) to bid for the trains; this was a joint venture between three national consortia and comprised:

Great Britain:

>GEC Transportation Projects Ltd
>British Rail Engineering Ltd
>Brush Electrical Machines Ltd
>Metropolitan Cammell Ltd

France:

>Alsthom SA
>De Dietrich et CIE
>ANF Industrie

Belgium:

>BN Constructions. Ferroviaires et Metalliques
>ACEC Transport SA

The division of work within the joint venture was established to ensure an equitable share both of the design work and of the manufacture. The mechanical design responsibility was given to the French consortium and the electrical design responsibility to the B itish consortium. A target split of 40:40:20 between the UK, France and Belgium was agreed.

Since the group was formed there have been many changes in the structure of the European railway industry and of the joint venture.

- Alsthom took over ACEC

- Metropolitan Cammell left the UK consortium

- Bombardier bought BN and ANF

- British Rail Engineering Ltd changed ownership and left the UK consortium

- GEC Power Engineering (including Transportation Projects Ltd) merged with Alsthom to form GEC ALSTHOM

- GEC ALSTHOM bought Metropolitan Cammell, which brought it back into the consortium

- ANF Industrie, withdrew from a manufacturing role

- Brush was bought by BTR.

The above changes made the organisation of the project very complicated. The main sites involved in the work are now:-

BOMBARDIER EURORAIL
Bruges:	trailer cars
Familleureux:	trailer cars

BRUSH ELECTRICAL MACHINES,
Loughborough:	traction motors

DE DIETRICH & CIE
Reichshoffen:	motored trailer cars

FAIVELEY TRANSPORT SA,

Tours: pantographs, electronic systems

GEC ALSTHOM

Aytré, La Rochelle: trailer cars
Belfort: power cars
Birmingham: trailer cars
Charleroi: auxiliary supplies and train control
Courbevoie, Paris: electronics
Le Creusot: bogies
La Défense, Paris: project management
Manchester: power and control electronics
Preston: electrical equipment
St Ouen, Paris: power transformers
Stafford: software and power transformers
Tarbes: electrical equipment
Villeurbanne: electronics

With the advantage of hindsight the factories and design offices producing the train are too numerous and geographically too spread out. Certain thyristor modules are made in Manchester from components bought from many suppliers; they are shipped 1300km to the French/Spanish border where they are assembled into a cubicle, transported 1000km to Strasbourg where the cubicle is installed in a vehicle which is delivered 800km by rail to La Rochelle; the vehicle is then coupled into an articulated rake before undertaking a 700km journey to Belfort where it is finally assembled into a train and tested. However, while it is possible to criticise the industrial structure as clumsy or overcomplex, it is difficult to envisage an alternative solution that would have been acceptable to all the interested parties in 1988.

MECHANICAL DESIGN

Mechanically the TMST is based on the French TGV Atlantique, which entered service in October 1989 on the new route from Paris to Bordeaux and Nantes. However, many changes have been incorporated to make it suitable for running through the Tunnel to London; the most obvious is that, because the British loading gauge is smaller than in mainland Europe, the train has had to be redesigned to reduce the width. This has affected not only the body but also the bogies which have been modified to reduce the overhang of the airsprings and dampers.

To maximise the amount of traffic through the Tunnel a very long train has been specified. The TGV-Atlantique trains have 10 coaches between a pair of power cars. The TMST will have 18 intermediate coaches making it a much heavier train requiring more power to maintain its full speed. Principal data are given in Table 1.

Each 20-car TGV-Transmanche will be formed of two identical half-trains back-to-back (Table 2) to give a total length of 394m. The end of each rake of nine articulated coaches sits on a non-articulated bogie. The bogie next to each power car is powered, with the associated traction equipment housed in a compartment in the coach directly above. This arrangement, similar to that on the Paris-Sud-Est TGVs, gives 12 powered axles per train.

Table 1: Principal characteristics of TMST

Length overall	394 m
Maximum width	2.8 m
Power car bogie centres	14 m
Trailer car bogie centres	18.7 m
Bogie wheelbase	3 m
Wheel diameter	0.920 mm
Weight in working order	752 tonnes
Weight when laden	816 tonnes
Adhesion weight	204 tonnes
Maximum speed in service	300 km/h
Continuous rating at 25kV	12.2 MW
Continuous rating at 3 kV	5.7 MW
Continuous rating at 675 kV	3.4 MW
Traction motor rating	12 x 1020 kW
Number of motored bogies	6
Number of trailer bogies	18

As with all TGVs, in order to be permitted to run at 300km/h on SNCF's high speed lines, the static axleload is limited to 17 tonnes. Axleloads throughout the train will be close to this limit.

Table 2: Composition of a TMST half-train

R1/18 Second class, non-smoking, 52 seats, equipment compartment, nursery area,
R2/17 Second class, non-smoking, 60 seats,
R3/16 Second class, non-smoking, 60 seats,
R4/15 Second class, smoking, 60 seats,
R5/14 Second class, smoking, 60 seats,
R6/13 Buffet-bar, 2 catering stores,
R7/12 First class, smoking, 39 seats, lounge area,
R8/11 First class, non-smoking, 39 seats, lounge area, telephone,
R9/10 First class, non-smoking, 27 seats, space and WC for disabled passengers, baggage compartment, 2 customs compartments

Total capacity: 794 seats (210 first, 584 second) plus 52 folding seats.

Platforms in France are about 500mm above the rail level and all main line trains have steps - only on the metro or RER are platforms the same height as the carriage floor. TMST has to be designed for boarding either from an SNCF platform or from a traditional 915mm high British Rail platform. In the Tunnel itself there will be a platform for emergency evacuation but it will be further from the track than is normal and the train has to cater for this eventuality. With the changed step design and the changed bodyside profile the doors for the TMST are completely new, although based on previous designs.

FIRE PRECAUTIONS

Because of the special requirements for Tunnel operation greater emphasis has been placed on the flame retardance of materials for use on the trains. The more stringent standards imposed for TMST and the need to ensure internationally acceptable certification has required testing or retesting most of the materials and of full size mock-ups of critical areas, such as fire barriers.

Inevitably, there have been problems in obtaining materials that can be demonstrated to meet the fire performance requirements and that have the necessary mechanical and acoustic properties but these have now been resolved.

To meet the safety requirements there has been a change in philosophy in many of the train systems. On a traditional train, safety systems are designed to stop the train in the event of any alarms. Although it is not hazardous to stop a train in the Tunnel, the logistics of evacuating passengers, the possibility of panic and the difficulty of sending maintenance staff or emergency services have made the rule "keep going if it is safe to do so". To meet this rule control systems and power equipment have been duplicated and special precautions have been adopted to ensure, as far as possible, that a single failure cannot stop the train. The price for this is that TMST is more complicated than other TGVs and the whole central communications system has had to be redesigned to increase capacity and redundancy. A mock-up of the complete network of more than 30 computers has been installed at the GEC ALSTHOM Research Centre at Stafford to prove the communications system before it is installed on the train.

The possibility that a fire might disable part of the traction equipment has been considered and the traction equipment has been designed to allow the train to exit from the Tunnel with only two out of six power bogies operating: that is, no traction at one end and one of three "motor blocs" at the other end disabled.

Should fire stop a train, it can be split to shed a damaged portion. For this purpose, the two power cars and the trailer rakes are four units which can be uncoupled from inside the train. If a power car is abandoned, the driver can then reconfigure the braking, computer and control systems in the rest of the train and leave the Tunnel.

ELECTRICAL EQUIPMENT

The power equipment has been completely redesigned in comparison with the previous generation of TGVs. In France there are two different supply voltages - 25kV ac (including the high speed lines) and 1500V dc on other lines. TMST has to cope with three different supply voltages - 25kV in France, 3000V dc in Belgium and 750V dc on the Network South East lines in the UK. The 750V supply is a radically new feature for TGVs as it requires pick-up shoes that collect current from a third rail and not a pantograph operating from an overhead line. These collector shoes have to be retracted on other lines, to prevent fouling the gauge, and earthed for safety reasons. A prototype of the 3-voltage power equipment was installed in an old SNCF locomotive (BB10003) and covered thousands of miles of testing during 1990. At the same time an old BR locomotive was fitted with TMST bogies to prove the current collection system from the third rail and a similar bogie was fitted to a TGV to demonstrate that the additional mass of the collector shoes is not detrimental to the high speed performance of

the bogies. High power tests have been carried out on the Preston test bed to investigate normal and abnormal operating conditions.

Like the TGV Atlantique, the TMST uses 3-phase motors. Unlike the TGV-A they are asynchronous motors fed by GTO inverters rather than synchronous motors fed from thyristor convertors.

The main transformer and inductors for the input filter are immersed in an aluminium tank of non-flammable silicon-based oil. The main cooling group is mounted above the transformer and handles two separate cooling circuits - for the transformer and the common bloc power semi-conductors. These, like other equipment on the train, are modular; individual modules can be simply withdrawn and plugged-in during maintenance; automatic quick-release fluid couplings ensure that there is no loss of cooling oil and there is no need to drain an entire system to replace a single module.

The traction system at each end of the train consists of three independent motor blocs, one for each power bogie. Two motor blocs are located at the rear of the power car and one in the equipment compartment of the adjacent trailer.

Each motor bloc is responsible for traction and rheostatic braking of the two motors of one power bogie, including its auxiliaries. Braking can be achieved in the absence of an external supply to the train. A motor bloc consists of one power inverter for each motor, control electronics, a brake link charger and its own auxiliaries.

The auxiliaries include cooling systems for the motor bloc power electronics, traction motors and for dissipation of energy generated in electrical braking. Modules similar to the common bloc modules are used for the motor bloc electronics.

The more powerful multivoltage equipment on TMST is intrinsically heavier and bulkier than the equipment on TGV-A. To save weight and space many functions have been carried out using micro-electronics instead of traditional electromechanical relays. The new designs have been proved on the test bed and on prototype vehicles. The power car body structure has been redesigned using computer analysis to save 15% of the structural weight.

CAB AND SIGNALLING EQUIPMENT

From the viewpoint of the train designer it would have been convenient if the 3 Railways (4 if Eurotunnel is included) could have standardised on signalling systems throughout their networks. Historically this did not happen and thus the TMST driving cab is one of the most sophisticated in the world. It features a computer console, pre-selection "cruise" speed control, and in addition, space has been found for an array of cab signalling systems. To meet the needs of all four railways (including Eurotunnel), the train will be equipped with TVM430, KVB and the "Crocodile" automatic warning system for use in France, TBL for running in Belgium, BR's AWS and, in due course, whatever automatic train protection BR adopts after current trials are concluded. Eurotunnel has adopted TVM430 for the Tunnel.

As SNCB develops TBL and BR implements ATP, it may well be that systems displaying information to the driver will converge. The cab equipment, including the programmable logic controllers driving the on-desk computer screen used for fault finding and predeparture tests, fills 4 full height 19" racks.

STANDARDS AND SPECIFICATIONS

All railways procure equipment against standards for design and construction. Many of these are the same between administrations but others are different. It was a major achievement that IPG managed to pull-together a consistent set of technical standards acceptable to the three Railways.

To define exactly how the train has to perform under normal and failure conditions, detailed specifications have been drafted for each function and discussed between the IPG and the contractors. As with other documentation on the project the thousands of pages of functional specifications had to be translated into English and French. Maintenance documentation also has to be translated into Flemish.

NORTH OF LONDON TRAINS

It is not possible for trains that are 394m long to operate north of London because at most stations the platforms cannot accept them. At one time, the intention was to split the trains and run them in two halves to different destinations but this proved impractical.

An Instruction to Proceed was given in December 1991 for seven special TMST, to provide services between Paris or Brussels and various cities north of London on BR's East Coast and West Coast main lines. Each will have four fewer intermediate cars, bringing passenger numbers down to 114 first and 464 standard class, 578 in all. At 320m, they will still be very long passenger trains compared with those that usually operate in Britain.

The power control system for the NoL trains are being redesigned to reduce the line current as the BR power system has a lower rating than that on SNCF lines.

Modifications are also being made to the traction control system to eliminate harmonic currents of certain critical frequencies that might otherwise interfere with the correct operation of reed relay track circuits. In addition, the train auxiliary system must be recabled to ensure that there are no significant train-induced DC currents in the rails.

The power car suspension is being modified to accept anti-roll bars which will limit vehicle sway and thus reduce pantograph movement in high winds. This is necessary because they will operate on BR 25kV lines, which have different geometric characteristics to those of SNCF and Eurotunnel.

Other than the relocation of certain electrical equipment because of the loss of four trailer cars, there is only one other significant change from the Three Capitals trains. The centre cars (R9 and R10) will have more accommodation for border control staff, allowing British customs and passport checks to be carried out on-board.

C451/027

The Channel Tunnel tourist wagons

I J MILLMAN, BSc, PEng
Project Implementation Division Eurotunnel, Coquelles, France

SYNOPSIS   This paper gives a general appreciation of the physical characteristics of the passenger
wagons to be used in Channel Tunnel operations. A number of special features of this rolling stock
are described as is the modus operandi for loading and unloading of motor vehicles. The Train
Captain and crew interface with passengers and special safety features is described.

1. INTRODUCTION

In order to comprehend the type of rail operation
foreseen between England and France in general,
and the type of Tourist Wagon equipment to be
used in particular, it might be best to say a few
words about each wagon type.   To be precise,
there are two types of wagons, Single Deck and
Double Deck, each of which can be broken down
into three categories, Loaders, 'A' type and 'S'
type carrier wagons.

Considering the Single Deck Carrier (SDC)
wagons first, we see from Figure 1 that these are
intended for the carriage of buses or coaches and
are dimensioned so as to accommodate the largest
vehicles in common use in Europe and the U.K.
The Single Deck Loader (SDL) shown in Figure 2 is
a relatively flat vehicle having a retractable
canopy and two full length loading bridges.
Thus, buses may load from either side.

Arrangements   in the Double-Deck Carriers
(DDC) are somewhat different. We see from Figure
3 that these are primarily used for the carriage
of private motor cars on an upper and lower deck.
Figure 4 shows the Double Deck Loader (DDL)
wagon.   Vehicles enter through loading doors and
go either to the lower deck or, by means of an
internal ramp, to the upper deck. Vehicles may
enter the Shuttle train from one or both sides.

The major significant difference between the
'A' and 'S' type wagon is that the 'A' has one
fully automatic coupler and one semi-permanent
coupler,   whereas   the   'S' type has two
semi-permanent couplers. Both types of carrier
wagon are built into a minimum replaceable unit -
the "triplette". This is composed of two 'A'
wagons surrounding an 'S' type as shown in Figure
5.

A "RAKE" is then formed by placing four
triplettes together and a loader at each end.
Two RAKES are joined to form a SHUTTLE when, of
course, a locomotive is added at each end.

The crew for each shuttle is quite unique.
There will be a driver who, quite conventionally,
operates the train from the leading locomotive.
However, there will also be a Chef de Train or
Train Captain travelling in the rear loco. As

his title implies, he is responsible for the safe
and efficient operation of the entire shuttle in
normal, degraded and emergency modes. The driver
(who is also trained as a Train Captain) will
operate under his supervision, as will the other
six members of the crew. The entire crew will be
trained in the operation of all shuttle systems
and will also be able to bring into operation a
number of back-up or emergency systems, under the
supervision of the Captain.

This completes our mini-tour of the tourist
wagons and crew, and we now take a quick look at
their relationship with the terminals and
tunnels.

2. TERMINAL/TUNNEL INTERFACES

One of the deciding factors in conceiving the
Channel Tunnel system was convenience in
access/egress to and from the Shuttle, which is
normally composed of one DDC and one SDC RAKE.
Traffic arriving at the terminals will be
segregated into vehicle groups suitable for SDC
or DDC operations. Crossing the tracks by an
overbridge, the vehicles will be brought into
single file on any one of eight platforms. Up to
sixty motor cars will be accommodated in each
deck of the RAKE so that up to 120 can be
transported in each trip. As for SDC operations,
twelve coaches can be accommodated in this RAKE.

The twin tunnels themselves and the full
length service tunnel, have been the subject of
numerous articles and need not delay us here
except in one respect. Reliability of service is
essential to the success of this operation and,
to this end, we are able to take advantage of two
cross-over areas in the under-sea section of the
tunnel.   Thus, if essential maintenance, an
incident or breakdown causes blockage in one
portion of one tunnel, then single line
operations can continue in both directions but at
slightly reduced frequency. Provided that they
are not in the same portion of the tunnel, we
can, in fact, accommodate two such blockages.
The service tunnel and its cross passages,
together with the special service vehicles
provide rapid access for men and equipment to any
troublesome area or train.

3. GROSS STATIC CHARACTERISTICS

Table 1 illustrates the vital statics of the six wagon types, but it must be admitted that these barren figures do little justice to these singularly complex and sophisticated wagons. Before revealing some of their secrets however, it would be inappropriate not to mention the single feature which they have in common -- non plus ultra - safety

	SDC	SDL	DDC	DDL
OVERALL LENGTH, m	26	26	26	28
OVERALL HEIGHT, m	5.6	5.6	5.6	5.6
DISTANCE BETWEEN BOGIE CENTRES, m	19	19	19	20
PORTAL OPENING HEIGHT, m	4.3	4.3	2	2
PORTAL OPENING WIDTH, m	3.3	3.3	3.3	3.3
MAX WEIGHT (TONS)	63	64	65	64.5
DECK HEIGHT, m	1.05	1.05	1.05	1.05
DECK LENGTH, m	23.1	-	23.2	-
AXLE LOADING TONNES	22	22	22	22
DESIGN SPEED, km/hr	160	160	160	160
QUANTITY	108	18	108	18

TABLE 1

Safety has been the dominant concern in their design as it will be in their operation, from bogies to roof, coupler to coupler. This will become evident as we complete our tour of these singular vehicles.

Let us take the SDC wagon first. Referring to Figure 1, we see that it is large enough to accommodate almost any current design of coach and the floor, which has up to twenty-four tonnes capacity, has built in kerbs to guide them safely through the wagons. At each end of the wagon are two door frames which can rotate about a vertical axis so as to provide clearance during loading. Before transit, the frames rotate into their normal position and a sliding shutter, or Fire Barrier, is lowered. Pneumatic seals ensure that the wagon is a sealed unit. However, access to other wagons may obtained by means of two sets of pass doors at each end of the wagon.

In order to avoid a vehicle impacting the Fire Barrier, thus potentially damaging and/or blocking it if a sudden deceleration occurs, a floor mounted Fire Barrier Protection Device is operated, raising suitable steel protection arms.

There are four Emergency Doors in the SDC - two each side. These are not normally operable during transit, but can be used for access to passenger egress platforms in cross-over areas if the need arises. They are pneumatically operated and are normally under the control of the Train Captain, though a manual mode is provided for.

Referring to Figure 2, we find that the SDL has two interesting features - a passenger amenity area and crew cabin. The amenity area has a double toilet and minor first aid facilities. The crew cabin has sufficient controls to permit shunting operations in the maintenance yard and local diagnostic activities.

The DDC shown in Figure 3 is externally similar in appearance to the SDC but is quite different internally. The DDC is divided longitudinally by an intermediate deck, so that vertical clearance is sufficient for the majority of current types of motor vehicles. The floor strength is not, of course, as high as the SDC, being only 12.5 tonnes/deck. Once again, there are kerbs to shepherd motor cars safely through the wagon. At each end of each deck there are door frames and fire barriers, each containing two sets of Pass Doors, providing convenient access from one wagon to another. Two unique features of the DDC 'S' wagon are that they have stairs between decks and a toilet facility on the lower deck.

The DDL shown in Figure 4 also has two notable features. Up to three Motorcycles may be accommodated on the lower deck, and an amenity area is provided for the riders on the upper deck. A crew cabin also permits local control of shunting operations during maintenance.

4. OPERATING CHARACTERISTICS

In order to illustrate the unique features of Channel Tunnel System operations, we will assume that a Shuttle has just completed unloading at a terminal. We will imagine that a stream of vehicles is now making its way onto the platform for embarkation.

Motor cars will be directed to one of two loading doors on the DDL of each rake and, crossing a bridge plate, they enter the loader. Half of the vehicles will proceed immediately ahead, passing through successive wagons until met by a crew member who will marshal them so as to park five vehicles per deck. The other half will proceed up a short ramp to gain access to their deck but the procedure is the same for them after that point. Note that since the two streams are proceeding in parallel, the loading process will be completed quite quickly. In order to deal with the fumes produced by cars making their way through the wagon, a powerful air "purging" system comes into operation at the commencement of loading.

As each wagon deck is filled, the crew member will command the door frames to close and the fire barrier to descend. The fire barrier protection devices will also operate. Shortly after completion of loading in each wagon, the purging system will shut down and a normal HVAC system will come into operation.

Passengers will be encouraged to remain in or near their vehicles during the trip, but access to a toilet will be provided as mentioned above. Public address messages will be made from time to time, informing passengers of progress during transit. These will occur either as audio messages or on dot-matrix panels located at each end of the wagon deck. Passengers may also tune their radio to an information channel available throughout the shuttle train.

Upon reaching the French terminal the loading process is reversed, each vehicle driving straight ahead in turn to complete the cycle.

The loading and transit phase for SDC operations is very similar to the double deck case but differences do exist as follows. To commence loading, the SDL canopy must first be withdrawn prior to loading and full length bridge plates lowered on either side. In addition, a propping system is operated in both loader and carrier wagons to ensure a stable surface while a bus or coach is manoeuvring on the loader wagon and moving through the carrier wagons. Once again, crew members will be on hand to marshal the buses and to close the fire barriers and ensure the propping system is retracted. An air purging system also operates during loading to remove unpleasant exhaust fumes.

5. MODES OF OPERATION

The Channel Tunnel Shuttle train will normally operate as a Double Deck RAKE and a Single Deck RAKE, consisting of four loader wagons, twenty four wagons and two locomotives. Alternatively, each train can just as conveniently be made up from two Single Deck or two Double Deck RAKES plus locomotives.

Within each of these possibilities, several alternatives exist to accommodate changing operational requirements, or market conditions. For instance, a minor fault on any wagon, e.g. a fire detection system sensor inoperative or an emergency door fault, would dictate that that wagon not be used by passengers during transit. An attempt might be made to correct the fault between transits but, failing this, the shuttle would continue in service until the end of the day before entering the maintenance area. A more serious problem such as a battery failure would be accommodated by changing the entire triplette upon reaching the other terminal.

During periods when the demand for service is reduced, the possibility of operating shuttles with three triplettes per RAKE is under active consideration. All normal and emergency services within the wagons would, however, be available. One other advantage of this scenario is that it will provide a pool of spare triplettes for scheduled maintenance periods during off peak periods.

Turning now to degraded modes of operation, we should first recognise that each locomotive is quite capable of pulling any fully laden train, including a dead locomotive, through the entire tunnel. In fact, one locomotive is capable of starting the train on the most severe slope without roll back. Another remote but possible scenario is the case where a portion of the catenary is damaged, or main power is entirely lost. In that case, diesel rescue units are available at both ends of the tunnel, consisting of two diesels back-to back with a scrubber wagon between them. This unit is capable of rescuing any fully laden shuttle train without significantly polluting the tunnel atmosphere thanks to the scrubber unit.

A more severe form of degraded operation occurs as a result of a bogie derailment. In this case, passengers are moved to the wagons on one side of the affected wagon, a decoupling is made between triplettes and the single locomotive with its reduced train proceeds to the nearest terminal. Meanwhile, a rescue crew is sent via the Service Tunnel to re-rail the incident bogie and the second locomotive then rescues the

remainder of the train. Should the derailment be severe, then a second decoupling is made, leaving the affected triplette in place and the other locomotive is used to remove the unaffected portion. The rescue diesel set will be used to remove the damaged wagons when appropriate.

One further point should be stressed. During these anomalous or emergency operations, the essential safety systems aboard the shortened train remain in full force. Should a fire break out during the rescue operation the full fire detection/extinction system is operative, as is video monitoring, together with audio and visual evacuation announcements.

Two other degraded forms of operation are accommodated by the unique design features of the shuttle system. A coupling failure resulting in a broken train would, under most circumstances produce a difficult situation, especially in a tunnel. In our case, the emergency brakes will operate, bringing the two portions to a halt. However, the Train Captain in the rear locomotive, and the original driver in his locomotive will be able to take control of their remaining portions. After appropriate co-ordination with central control they may then drive their locomotives to the nearest cross-over or to the nearest terminal for disembarkation of passengers.

The two cross-over caverns, situated at approximately the $1/3$ distance points of the undersea crossing provide the next link in the chain of safety during emergency operations. Should a serious incident occur during transit, the primary objective is to remove the train from the tunnel, assuming that it is fully mobile. However, an incident leaving doubt about the safety of the passengers will be dealt with by a full passenger disembarkation at the nearest cross-over cavern where full length platforms and emergency facilities are available. If, however, the train is completely immobilised then disembarkation can take place at any point in the tunnel onto a walkway.

6. INTERNAL SYSTEMS

The objective here is to describe not so much the conventional systems, but those which are unique to the Channel Tunnel Tourist Wagons and we should start by considering the Train Captain's Desk as shown in Figure 6. Situated in the locomotive, it is not strictly part of the Tourist Wagon, but its design is such that it forms an essential and unique feature of the entire train. Available to the Train Captain is a wide variety of inputs from the entire length of the train transmitted to him via a computer controlled digital network. The data is displayed on an interactive TV type format and the Captain has a number of modes in which he can operate. For the most part, during transit, he will operate in a monitoring mode where essential operating and safety related data will be annunciated. During loading and unloading, he will, of course, be interested to ensure that a smooth interface occurs between drivers, vehicles, crew members and wagon systems. Between transits he will be able to investigate, in considerable detail, any failures detected during a previous passage or run test programmes to ensure proper functioning of equipment.

The data available is, broadly speaking, divided into two types, Intelligent and Non-Intelligent systems. The first of these not only provides status input, but will accept commands to modify its performance and provide verification that this command has been implemented. The Non-Intelligent systems provide status data only.

Another of the screens is available to the Train Captain displaying the video signals obtained from two cameras on each deck of all wagons. The screens are split so as to show all camera inputs from one deck simultaneously. A sequencing device permits the Captain to view each wagon in turn. However, he can also select any deck, so as to view the loading/unloading operation for instance. There is also an automatic select feature where an incident occurs, i.e., fire alarm is detected in any wagon.

The Train Captain also has a range of communication features. He has direct communication with central Control and with Crew Members via the Shuttle Internal Radio. He can address any one, any triplette, any RAKE or the entire shuttle train by P.A., initiate a set sequence of pre-recorded announcements both by P.A. and dot-matrix panels, or respond directly to a call made by any passenger on any of the two call boxes situated on each wagon deck.

Primary power is supplied as 1500V DC 750 KVA trainline from each locomotive passing through the automatic coupler, returning through the rails. During passage of a neutral section, the affected locomotive supply is disconnected and load shedding occurs to avoid power demand in excess of 750 KVA.

The primary power is used by solid state inverters to generate two separate 400 V AC supplies in each 'A' wagon, a 110 V DC supply and a battery charge circuit. Each power supply is fully protected from over-voltage and short circuit conditions. The batteries are sized to provide at least 90 minutes operation of all essential services and provide an alarm signal to the Train Captain if at any time their charge is insufficient for this purpose.

Air Conditioning is an essential part of the Tourist Wagon design since the train will operate in a wide range of temperature and humidity conditions while in the tunnel. The HVAC units are sized to provide a comfortable environment during both summer and winter operations by including both closed and open loop operation. Even the amenity areas in the Single Deck and Double Deck loader have their own HVAC systems.

7. SAFETY SYSTEMS

The Fire Detection/Extinction (FDE) System used in all tourist wagons is, simply, second to none. No other system currently employed in public transportation in general and in rolling stock in particular can match it for performance or efficiency. The following remarks will be intended as a guide, since a full description would take up far too much time.

The fire detection system is composed of a number of detectors disposed throughout the body of the wagon. If a fire does occur and any <u>two</u> detectors are triggered, the Train Captain is alerted and crew members are dispatched to investigate and deal with the situation. The HVAC system is automatically shut down to prevent mixing of fresh air and fumes.

If passenger evacuation to adjacent wagons is necessary, audio and visual instructions for this activity are given. The FDE still continues to monitor the situation and, by now, crew members are on hand to help passengers or aid handicapped persons.

Should the situation continue to deteriorate an automatic discharge of Halon occurs. This will, of course, mix fumes with the remaining air, but will extinguish the fire. However crew members have breathing apparatus available to re-enter the affected wagon to make sure that all remaining passengers are safely evacuated.

The FDE also deals with potential dangers before they can become a menace. It does this by detecting flammable hydrocarbon gas levels in the air and in the wagon drainage system. Once again, a series of increasing alarms will first of all trigger the purging system to lower any combustible gas concentration but if a dangerously high concentration is detected, the purging system is arrested and a Halon discharge occurs. If a fire breaks out on the floor area due to a fuel leak, then an automatic two part foam discharge system is operated. A fluid foam washes liquid fuel into the drainage area where an aspirated foam snuffs out any fuel fed fire.

The systems mentioned above are entirely automatic and will, if necessary, deal with fire or explosive gas incidents without crew intervention. It should be noted, however, that there are also two passenger fire alarm points per deck, operation of which will place the automatic system in an extra alert state. In addition, there are two portable fire extinguishers per deck to deal with minor incidents.

One last point about the FDE concerns its reliability. Excessive false alarms are, after all, as potentially dangerous as a failure to produce an alarm. In order to avoid this situation, the FDE requires at least two detectors (or one detector plus one manual alarm) to initiate automatic action, as mentioned before. Moreover, the FDE is, itself split into two redundant systems so that the likelihood of a non- detected fire due to system failure is exceedingly small.

The FDE is backed up by a number of successive levels of safety engineering. For instance, the floor, walls and roof are specifically designed and tested to withstand the effects of a major fire for more than 30 minutes without significant structural failure, giving adequate time for the train to be withdrawn from the tunnel.

The fire barriers at the end of each deck will also provide a minimum of thirty minutes passenger protection from flames, fumes or excessive temperatures to passengers who have been evacuated to an adjacent wagon. In addition, the inter-wagon gangway will provide a sealed area through which it is unlikely that a fire could propagate itself.

Each deck is fitted with Emergency Doors which are normally under the control of the Train Captain. However, if due to loss of communication, electrical or pneumatic power he is not able to operate them, a manual back up system is always available.

If should also be noted that all of the safety features mentioned above, including FDE, Public Address, Dot Matrix panels, Emergency Instruction panels and lighting are available irrespective of crew input. Batteries will provide a minimum of ninety minutes continuous use, sufficient time for the train to be evacuated from the tunnel, or rescue forces to reach the exceedingly rare case of a stranded train.

8. CONCLUSION

In this paper, we have taken what can only be described as a superficial glance at some of the more interesting and unique features of the Tourist Wagons. It would be unfortunate if the impression is left that these features operate in complete isolation. The quintessential feature of those systems, particularly the safety features, is their linking in such a way as to provide several levels of both automatic and inter-active crew initiated actions designed to lead to an optimally safe operation. Selective but wide spread redundancies make the possibility vanishingly small that an incident will, itself, trigger a more serious situation.

These wagons represent at technical leap of the imagination, as does the tunnel itself. They may become models for future generations of passenger vehicles providing comfortable and safe transportation well into the next millennium.

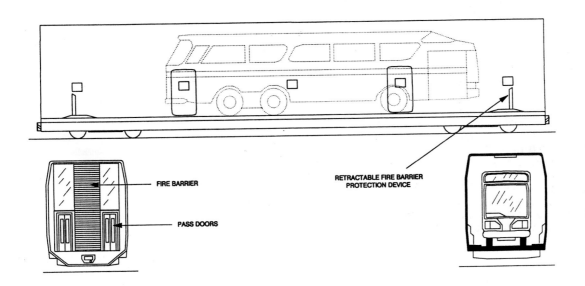

Figure 1 - SINGLE DECK CARRIER WAGON

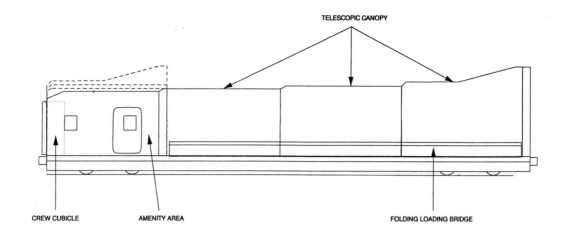

Figure 2 - SINGLE DECK LOADER WAGON

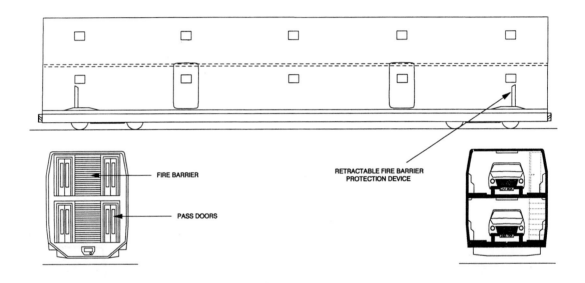

Figure 3 - DOUBLE DECK CARRIER WAGON

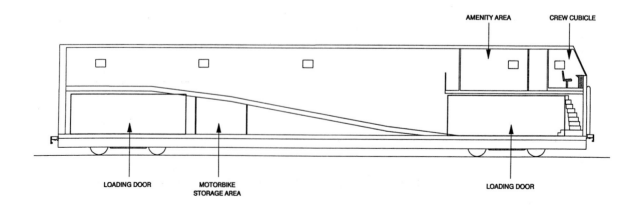

Figure 4 - DOUBLE DECK LOADER WAGON

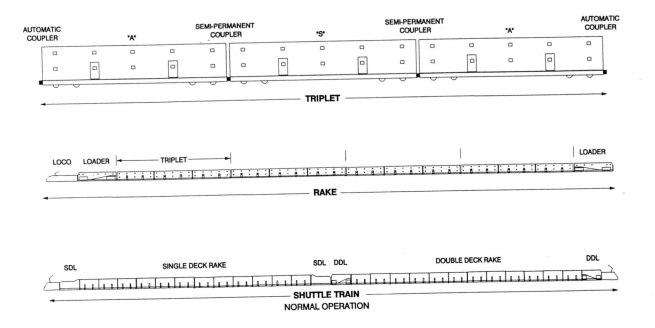

Figure 5 - SHUTTLE TRAIN CONFIGURATION

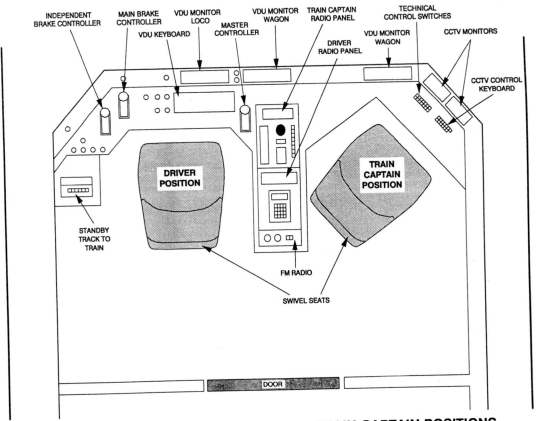

Figure 6 - SHUTTLE TRAIN DRIVER AND TRAIN CAPTAIN POSITIONS

C451/021

Channel Tunnel Nightstock — the name of the game is compatibility

I C ROCLIFFE, BSc, CEng, MIMechE
European Passenger Services, Derby

SYNOPSIS

Nightstock is being built to operate high quality overnight services between the United Kingdom and the Continent, via the Channel Tunnel.

i)   It will work over a large part of the BR network and so must be compatible with new and existing traction and infrastructure.

ii)   Operation through the Channel Tunnel demands essential systems and abilities in areas such as fire safety, communications and control, emergency uncoupling and access/egress. But the Tunnel is, of course, only a means to an end, the aim being to reach destinations on the Continent.

iii)   Once through the Tunnel, Nightstock must be run like any other International locomotive-hauled train. Hence, a third set of requirements apply to allow operation with UIC traction and coaching stock and Continental infrastructure.

The combination of these three very different sets of compatibility requirements (BR, Channel Tunnel, the Continent) produces some unique problems and a unique train.

1   INTRODUCTION

1.1   Why consider Nightstock and its compatibility features?. Quite simply, it will be a unique train. Aside from the obvious distinction of being part of the pioneering Channel Tunnel project, Nightstock will be different from the high speed Class 373 day trains (TMST). TMST's are self-contained unit trains operating over part of the BR electrified network through to Paris and Brussels, and represent a joint project between three Railways. Nightstock, on the other hand, is locomotive-hauled and is the result of five Railways agreeing on a business opportunity to run overnight services between centres around a wider BR network (including non-electrified routes) and France, Belgium, the Netherlands and Germany. As a result, Nightstock has to be uniquely 'universal' in nature, allowing it to integrate with a very wide range of existing operating and infrastructure requirements in the United Kingdom and on the Continent, while satisfying the additional and stringent demands for operating through the Channel Tunnel. Thus the apparently continuous journey from, say, Swansea to Paris provides the engineers with three sets of technical challenges according to geographical location:

i   BR network

ii   Channel Tunnel

iii   Continental (UIC) network.

1.2   BR Network

Figure 1 shows the wide extent of Nightstock's operation over the BR network, where it must function as conventional locomotive-hauled stock. It must therefore be compatible with:

-   The new Class 92 locomotive (its main source of traction).

-   Existing locomotives.

-   New infrastructure (eg Waterloo International Station, North Pole International Depot).

-   Existing infrastructure (gauging, track, platforms, depots).

- Existing operating
  requirements (eg door control,
  on-train communications,
  emergency equipment,
  access/egress, etc).

1.3 Channel Tunnel

Specific requirements apply to
all passenger stock operating
through the Channel Tunnel
including:

- Stringent fire safety
  requirements.

- Communications systems.

- Emergency uncoupling facility.

- Control functions (eg
  passenger alarm indications to
  driver, ability to close fresh
  air intakes, etc).

- Parking brake requirements.

- Access/egress requirements.

- Protection of essential
  systems from illegal use.

- Complete 'sealing' of the
  train from a security point of
  view.

- Elimination of hiding places
  for illegal substances.

1.4 Continental (UIC) Network

Once through the Tunnel,
Nightstock must operate like any
other International
locomotive-hauled train. UIC
Specifications define the
requirements here, and cover
compatibility with the following:

- UIC standard locomotives.

- UIC standard coaching stock.

- Continental infrastructure
  (gauging, track, platforms,
  depots).

- Operating requirements (eg
  door control, communications,
  parking brake, etc).

1.5 It is the range of compatibility
requirements which makes
Nightstock unique, and the scope
of these requirements can be seen
from Table 1. This paper focuses
on some of the most interesting
areas of the train, examines how
the differing constraints combine
and looks at some possible design
solutions.

2 BUSINESS SPECIFICATION

2.1 It is important to identify the
key points of the Business
Specification for Nightstock in
order to understand the technical
compatibility constraints and
their proposed resolution.

2.2 Services

See Figure 1.

One each way, nightly between:

London - Amsterdam
London - Germany.

One each way, nightly between:

Glasgow }   { Paris
Swansea } - {
Plymouth }   { Brussels

2.3 Accommodation

Three alternative levels:

- Sleeper with shower and
  toilet.

- Sleeper with toilet.

- Reclining seat.

2.4 Vehicle Types

- Sleeper

- Seated

- Service.

2.5 Fleet Size

120 vehicles plus maintenance
spares, plus operational spares
(139 total).

2.6 The Train

- Maximum speed 200km/hr.

- Conventionally bogied.

- Locomotive-hauled.

- Semi-permanently coupled
  sub-sets of seven or eight
  vehicles.

- 23m long vehicles.

- 'Networker' profile:

  38mm wider at cantrail than BR
  MkIII coach.

  80mm wider at waist than BR
  MkIII coach.

© IMechE 1992 C451/021

- London services:

2 x sub-sets	5 sleepers	200
	1 service	1
	2 seated	200
Train total customers		401

- Beyond London services:

  See Figure 4.

2 x sub-sets	3 sleepers	120
	1 service	1
	3 seated	300
Train total customers		421

- Trains can also comprise a single sub-set.

- Trains in the Channel Tunnel will consist of two sub-sets with a locomotive at each end.

2.7 Sleeper Vehicle

Six Category A compartments:

- One or two bunks.

- En-suite toilet and shower.

Four Category B compartments:

- One or two bunks.

- En-suite toilet.

All compartments convert to day time use providing two comfortable seats and table space.

Individually controlled air-conditioning.

Adjustable lighting.

Attendant call system.

2.8 Seated Vehicle

Reclining seats for 50 customers.

Raised 2 + 1 layout (three seats across vehicle).

Luggage storage below each seat and in overhead racks.

Three toilets per vehicle.

2.9 Service Vehicle

Catering.

Lounge and bar.

Disabled persons sleeping compartment with en-suite toilet.

Parcels and baggage area.

Two Frontier Control Authorities compartments.

Train Manager's office.

3 ACHIEVING MULTI-COMPATIBILITY

3.1 Various systems (some of which are discussed in more detail below) need to perform or be configured in a particular way. To achieve this a Sensing and Change-over System monitors various signals and services to produce an unambiguous assessment of the train state; (See Table 2)

This assessment is then used to configure the relevant train systems to be compatible with, or to produce the necessary functions for, the network on which the train is operating at the time.

3.2 Other compatibility requirements are satisfied simply by fitting dual (or more) sets of equipment and manually selecting the ones required on a particular network. An example of this approach occurs with the inter-vehicle connections fitted at the outer ends of Nightstock's sub-sets, as illustrated by Figure 2. There is obviously a spatial limit to how far this policy can be applied and Figure 2 shows an area close to that limit.

3.3 A third means for achieving multi-compatibility is for a system to deliver a single composite performance which meets all needs. This approach is used for the bogie and suspension system, vehicle structure and HVAC.

4 INTERFACE WITH OTHER TRACTION AND COACHING STOCK

4.1 BR Requirements

Nightstock is required to operate with:

- The new Class 92 locomotive.

- Existing ac electric locomotives.

- Existing diesel locomotives.

4.2 Channel Tunnel Requirements

The Class 92 locomotive will be the only service interface requirement here. However, operation through the Tunnel requires that trains can be automatically uncoupled, from within the train, for each of the following cases:

i To split the train in half, ie sub-set from sub-set.

ii To separate the train
(consisting of two sub-sets)
from either the front or rear
locomotive.

4.3 Continental Requirements

Nightstock must operate with:

- UIC standard locomotives.

- UIC standard coaching stock.

4.4 Proposed Solution

See Figure 2. Mechanical
coupling between sub-sets and
between locomotives and sub-set
will be by screw coupler and side
buffers, to UIC Specification,
which also satisfies BR's
requirements. The emergency
uncoupling requirement represents
a significant design challenge
when combined with the use of
such a conventional coupling
system. One solution is to split
the drawbar on the healthy part
of the train, between the
coupling hook and tail pin to
leave the hook section and screw
coupler attached to the draw hook
on the failed vehicle.

A gangway connection is required
at the ends of sub-sets to
provide regular passenger access
between sub-sets and to/from UIC
coaching stock when operating in
mixed trains on the Continent.
An improved passenger environment
is sought in this area compared
with the rather crude UIC 'rubber
ring' gangway and this, coupled
with the desirability of pressure
sealing, suggests a type of
gangway developed by DB giving
compatibility with standard UIC
gangways but offering a high
level of sealing. This type of
gangway uses a wide face plate to
prove a sealing surface and has
implications for the siting of
the body end equipment shown in
Figure 2. This reconciliation is
currently the subject of detailed
design work.

Inter-vehicle services
(electrical power, control and
pneumatics) are tackled in the
manner described in Point 3.2
above. The facility to break
these connections during
emergency uncoupling requires
special pull-out features (or
switching) which will preserve
the electrical integrity of the
healthy portion of the train.

5 INTERFACE WITH INFRASTRUCTURE

5.1 BR Requirements

Gauging requirements are set
primarily by the kinematic
envelope approach.

Passenger stepping distances to
platforms must not exceed the
following dimensions:

- Horizontal   275mm

- Vertical   250mm

- Diagonal   350mm.

5.2 Channel Tunnel Requirements

No special gauging restrictions
apply in the Channel Tunnel; the
size of the Shuttle trains far
exceeds that of conventional BR
and UIC vehicles.

Maximum stepping distance to the
emergency walkway are:

- Horizontal   350mm

- Vertical   250mm

- Diagonal   423mm

5.3 Continental Requirements

UIC gangway requirements apply a
standard 'referenced profile',
shifted by an amount which
depends on vehicle suspension
parameters to give a
'construction profile'. Certain
concessions are then permitted
beyond this construction profile,
according to other UIC
Specifications.

Although each Continental Railway
has its own standard platform
position, UIC Specifications do
not define maximum stepping
distance criteria. Therefore,
agreement has to be obtained with
each Administration on the
compatibility of a proposed
arrangement of passenger access
steps with their platforms.

5.4 Proposed Solution

The BR and UIC gauging
requirements have been applied
simultaneously, with the BR
criteria generally forming the
ruling case.

The combined requirements for maximum BR and Tunnel stepping distances, compatibility with Continental platforms and UIC gauging require a complex mobile step arrangement, which is deployed to one of two positions depending on the train state (See 3.1). On BR, a single mobile step is deployed. In Channel Tunnel and UIC modes the same step is deployed but to a different position (closer to the vehicle centre line) together with a lower mobile step to provide access to the Tunnel walkway and Continental platforms.

Figure 3 shows the mobile step arrangement. Accommodating the mechanism for such an arrangement within the very limited space available below the external doors and outboard of the bogie represents another major design challenge.

6 FIRE SAFETY

6.1 BR Requirements

Following experiences such as the Taunton Sleeper fire in 1978 and the Kings Cross fire in 1987, BR applies stringent fire safety requirements. The key document here is BS6853. This requires that key areas of the train must be protected by fire barriers (eg sleeping compartments, catering areas), materials of limited combustibility and smoke production characteristics must be used and a fire detection system is required to protect all sleeping compartments. In addition, the measures adopted on existing vehicles set an important precedent; for Nightstock, the Mk III sleeper forms an important minimum standard for fire safety.

6.2 Channel Tunnel Requirements

The primary objective for operation through the Tunnel is to keep a train moving in the event of a fire so that it can be tackled outside the Tunnel.

Consequently, additional requirements apply for fire barriers of thirty minutes duration in all floors and at the ends of all vehicles. The latter means that sliding doors of the same integrity as the fire barrier are required at gangways to allow through access to passengers. All systems which could cause the train to stop in the event of a fire must also be protected for a period of thirty minutes. A staff-operated fire alarm system covering all parts of the train is also included in the Tunnel operating requirements.

6.3 Continental Requirements

The most significant standard here is the French National Standard NFF16-101 which deals with materials. It takes a different approach to that of the British Standard, and categorises materials by combustibility and smoke generation indices. The acceptability of materials depends upon a balance between these two criteria.

6.4 Proposed Solution

The principle was established with the TMST, and accepted by the Inter-Governmental Safety Authority, that the constructor should have the choice between the British and French Standards for material selection, but not a mixture of the two. On Nightstock, NFF16-101 is to be used. However, vehicles will also meet the constructional and fire detection requirements of BS6853 (See 6.1) and all the requirements (both constructional and communications) imposed for Channel Tunnel operation (See 6.2.).

7 VEHICLE STRUCTURE

7.1 BR Requirement

The BR proof load cases for the vehicle body structure are now well established, setting values applied as either point or distributed loads at various positions on the underframe and body end. The structure must withstand these loads without permanent deformation and full scale proof load tests are usually carried out on a pre-production bodyshell. These requirements are, in most respects, common to those set by UIC.

For fatigue design, BR traditionally uses the method given in BS5400 Part 10.

Largely as a result of the Clapham accident in 1988, BR now insists on additional so-called 'crashworthiness' requirements as follows:

i   In the event of a collision between vehicle ends, the structure must collapse preferentially from the ends, without forming a 'ramp' which may promote over-riding.

ii   A minimum of 0.5MJ has to be absorbed by the collapsing structure when loaded across the body end at waist level. The maximum collapse distance to achieve this is 1m.

iii A minimum of 1MJ has to be absorbed by the collapsing structure when loaded across the full vehicle end wall. The maximum collapse distance to achieve this is also 1m.

iv   All intermediate couplers must collapse at compressive loads in excess of between 1800kN and 2000kN, so bringing adjacent vehicle ends together and bringing into play an anti-shear system which resists lateral and vertical relative movement between vehicle ends.

v   The end wall must be able to withstand a point load of 150kN applied at any position on its edge (ie where it meets the bodyside).

Points i to v above all stem from BR's experience of the behaviour of vehicles in collisions and attempt to prevent the intrusion of one vehicle's structure into the passenger or crew space of another.

7.2 Channel Tunnel Requirements

There are no special structural requirements for operation through the Channel Tunnel.

7.3 Continental Requirements

As mentioned in Point 7.1 above, the UIC Specification for body structures is very similar to that which is now adopted by BR. No special 'crashworthiness' measures are specified. Fatigue design is by use of the Goodman Diagram method.

7.4 Proposed Solution

Design details are not established at present, but the approach to this area will be structure which meets a combination of requirements, in the manner described in Point 3.3. The one exception to this is in the area of fatigue design where the constructor has elected to use the BS5400 method.

8 ELECTRICAL SUPPLIES

8.1 BR Requirements

The BR electric train supply system (ETS) is two-pole, ie two conductors are proved down the length of the train, supplied from the locomotive with either ac or dc from the range 400V to 1500v, depending on the type of locomotive.

The Class 92 locomotive sets both the lower and upper limits of this range:

i   When operating over the third rail electrified routes of Network SouthEast, the Class 92 locomotive supplies the third rail voltage to the ETS system, this can be as low as approximately 400V dc.

ii   When operating on 25kV overhead electrified routes, the ETS is at a nominal voltage of 1500V ac.

Existing BR electric locomotives provide an ETS supply of nominal 1000V ac. The standard BR ETS jumper gear has a maximum current rating of 700A continuous, or 800A for one hour.

8.2 Channel Tunnel Requirements

Nightstock will be hauled through the Tunnel by the Class 92 locomotive, supplying an ETS of 1500v ac, using the standard BR jumper gear.

8.3 Continental Requirements

The Continental ETS system is single-pole, ie one conductor is carried down the length of the train (using a pair of paralleled jumpers between vehicles) with the return being via the running rails to the locomotive. Various supply voltages may be present depending on the network:

- 1000V ac

- 1500V dc

- 1500V ac

- 3000V dc.

The current rating of UIC standard ETS jumper equipment varies depending on ambient temperature.

8.4 Proposed Solution

The sensing and changeover system determines the correct configuration (ie one-pole or two-pole supply) by using contactors to connect each vehicle's electrical system appropriately, see Figure 4. It is important to ensure the electrical separation of the BR and UIC systems for reasons of safety.

The major component in the auxiliary system is the static converter. The first input stage of the converter will be a rectifier to deal with both ac and dc supplies. Details of how converters will cope with the range of possible input voltages are being developed.

It is essential to keep ETS currents within the maximum capacity of the jumper equipment in use, and this problem increases as the supply voltage falls. Currents are monitored and a load shedding regime is brought into operation, acting on all vehicles simultaneously, to switch loads in a series of pre-set stages. In an attempt to limit the power required whilst in-service, heating of shower water takes place while the vehicles are being pre-heated, in the depot.

9 CONTROL

9.1 BR Requirements

For existing BR locomotives there are no requirements for an electrical control interface (although there are some communication needs).

The control interface with the Class 92 locomotive is via a new 61-way jumper, which provides control and proving of doors, electro-pneumatically (EP) assisted brakes, verification of locomotive mode to the train (Channel Tunnel, BR third rail dc or BR 25kV), indications to the driver of passenger alarms or emergency door openings, certain end to end train wires for locomotive remote multiple operation and various other communication functions.

9.2 Channel Tunnel Requirements

It is possible for the driver in the Class 92 to close all fresh air intakes to the train in the event of smoke in the Tunnel. This is achieved via a signal on the 61-way control system.

9.3 Continental Requirements

Nightstock must operate, via the UIC standard 13-way control jumper, with the control system used by UIC locomotives and coaching stock for:

- Door control

- Lighting control.

In addition, the EP assisted braking system used by DB utilises this jumper and Nightstock must also be compatible with this. The SNCF EP assisted system, which is gaining acceptance across the Continent, uses a separate 4-way jumper; this forms another compatibility requirement for Nightstock.

9.4 Proposed Solution

Reference to Figure 2 shows the range of hardware required to achieve compatibility with all the systems highlighted above. The detail design of each control system is being progressed at present.

10 BRAKES

10.1 BR Requirements

BR's requirements for service brake performance are comparable with those for UIC. There are no requirements for a parking brake system on individual vehicles, the traditional approach being to use wheel scotches to secure single vehicles when parked.

10.2 Channel Tunnel Requirements

A requirement exists for a sub-set of eight vehicles to be parked on the maximum Channel Tunnel gradient of 11°/₀₀ in the worst conditions of low adhesion and a 30m/s headwind. This must be without assistance from the service brake and must be initiated by a single action by one member of staff.

10.3 Continental Requirements

See the comments in Point 10.1 above on service brake performance. The UIC requirement for parking brakes is for each vehicle to be equiped with a manually applied 'screw' brake, operated by a hand wheel located in the vestibule.

A DB requirement also exists for a magnetic track brake, in accordance with a UIC standard.

Both DB and SNCF have a requirement for an EP assisted braking system. By this system, electrical control signals derived from the locomotive can instruct all vehicles to either:

i   Apply the brakes by venting the brake pipe locally on each vehicle.

Or:

ii   Release the brakes by charging the brake pipe from the reservoir pipe locally on each vehicle.

The SNCF system uses a separate 4-way jumper system for the electrical control, whereas the DB system utilises the UIC standard 13-way control jumper and lines. In the event of failure of any part of the EP assisted system, the brakes operate as a conventional two pipe automatic air brake.

10.4 Proposed Solution

All axles will be equipped with three brake discs. One bogie on each vehicle will be equipped with a UIC screw brake arrangement, acting on one disc on each axle. On certain vehicles, the other bogie will be fitted with a similar parking brake mechanism, actuated by a spring-applied, body-mounted cylinder in order to meet the Channel tunnel parking brake requirement (See Point 10.2 above). Control of this system could be pneumatic or electrical.

Each bogie will be fitted with two electro-magnetic track brakes, one per side. These will be applied in response to an emergency brake application, directly onto the running rail head, energised by a supply taken from the vehicle's battery.

In order to take advantage of the EP assisted braking system, the Class 92 locomotive will be fitted with the necessary equipment to operate this system via the 61-way control jumper (See Point 9.1 above).

11 CONCLUSION

It is only possible to scratch the surface of a topic as complex as the Nightstock Specification in a paper such as this, and there are many areas which have not been explored. However, hopefully the above descriptions will give an indication of the scope of the demands which must be met if Nightstock is to achieve its objective. There is no doubt that the combination of compatibility requirements creates a tough challenge for the engineers, but once proven, Nightstock should become the shape of things to come.

TABLE 1: Scope of Compatibility Requirements

AREA	BR	CHANNEL TUNNEL	CONTINENT
Interfaces			
Other T & RS	*	*	*
Infrastructure			
- Gauging	*	-	*
- Track	*	-	*
- Steps	*	*	*
Fire Safety			
- Materials	See 6:	Fire Safety	
- Construction	C	C	-
- Protection of Essential Systems	-	*	-
- Fire Detection	C	C	-
Security			
Protection of Essential Systems	-	*	-
Hiding places	-	*	-
Structure	*	-	*
Gangways	-	-	*
Bogie & Suspension	*	-	*
Electric Train Supply	*	-	*
Control	*	*	*
Brakes			
- Service	C	C	C
- Parking Brake	-	*	*
- Track Brake	-	-	*
Doors	*	*	*
Communications	*	*	*
HVAC	*	*	*

*	Unique Requirements
C	Common Requirements
–	No Special Requirements

TABLE 2: **Train State**

LOCOMOTIVE PRESENT	TRAIN STATE
Existing BR locomotive	BR
Class 92 locomotive in BR mode	BR
Class 92 locomotive in Tunnel mode	Tunnel
UIC locomotive	UIC
No locomotive	No change from previous state

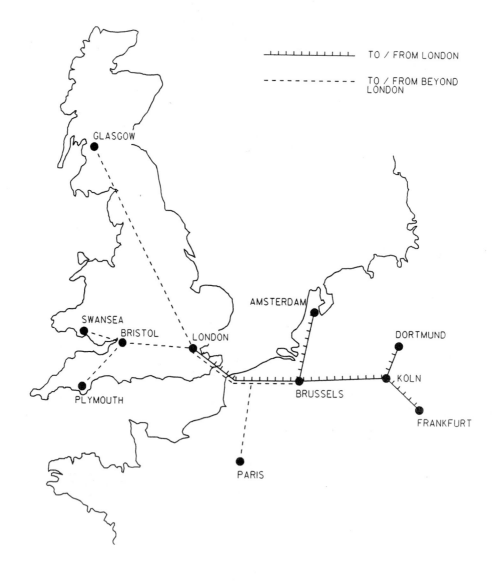

FIG I PROPOSED NIGHT SERVICES

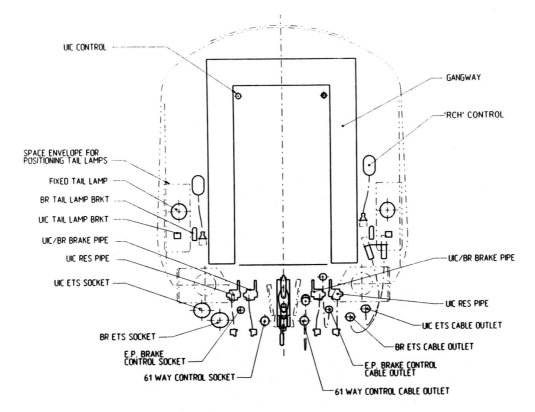

FIG 2   EQUIPMENT AT SUB-SET END

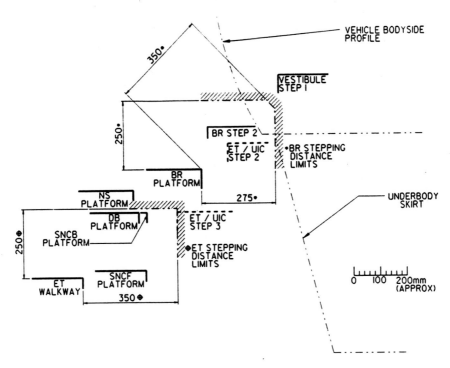

FIG 3   MOBILE STEP ARRANGEMENT AND
STANDARD PLATFORM POSITIONS

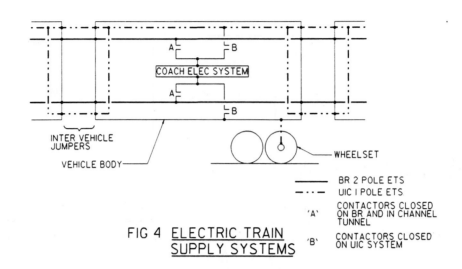

INTER VEHICLE
JUMPERS

VEHICLE BODY

COACH ELEC SYSTEM

WHEELSET

FIG 4 ELECTRIC TRAIN
       SUPPLY SYSTEMS

———— BR 2 POLE ETS
—··— UIC I POLE ETS

'A'   CONTACTORS CLOSED
      ON BR AND IN CHANNEL
      TUNNEL

'B'   CONTACTORS CLOSED
      ON UIC SYSTEM

Low track force technology bogies

M E BARHAM
Powell Duffryn Standard Limited, Cirencester, Gloucestershire

SYNOPSIS: Low Track Force bogies provide the opportunity for faster, quieter freight wagons which reduce the damaging effect of the wheel/rail forces on to the track infrastructure as well as providing the opportunity for increased payload.

1.0 INTRODUCTION:

In the early 1980's, British Rail Research initiated a research programme specifically aimed at reducing dynamic forces on freight bogies to enable a combination of higher speeds and higher axle loads to be accepted on existing vehicles without increasing track damage. This research was eventually transferred from BR Research to the private sector. Out of this exercise has grown the development of the Gloucester LTF bogie and its successful introduction into operational service in the United Kingdom where some 400 bogies are now working. (figure 1)

(fig 1. RfD Lowliner with LTF 13 bogies)

The development of the LTF also coincided with the advent of the Channel Tunnel and thus the interests of those National Railway Administrations on the other side of the Channel became increasingly important to us, since if we were to succeed with this development then we had to have their positive support and acceptance of what we were doing.

As in many other major technical developments, the problem of achieving ultimate acceptance can nearly represent as great a problem as finding the solution to the problem in the first place. Indeed, this problem can be exacerbated when the development in question contravenes some of the fundamental rules it should in fact be respecting. Imagine what it would have been like if Sir Frank Whittle, the father of the modern jet engine, had been required to meet the rules applicable to the performance and standards of a reciprocating engine ! Thus what I shall be talking about today is a story of technical development and technical achievement coupled with an outline of the detailed technical discussions which we have held with the Engineers of many of Europe's leading railways which have led to the approval in principle of LTF technology.

This paper is intended to explain the background to LTF technology, and it is also intended to be a paper which raises certain questions.

2.0 WHAT DO WE MEAN BY LOW TRACK FORCE ?

It will be will appreciated that two options exist to reduce the dynamic force levels. The first is to improve the suspension design to reduce the level of dynamic suspension forces caused by the motion of the vehicle body and bogie and the second is to reduce the P2 dynamic force (see note 1).

In order to achieve this P2 criterion a reduction in the unsprung mass is required. This was achieved in two ways; firstly by reducing the wheel diameter for a given axle load and secondly by putting the wheel bearings inside the wheels rather than following the traditional method of having the bearings on the outside of the wheels.

This combination of a reduced wheel diameter and a shorter axle length immediately gave a reduction of around 30-35 per cent in the weight of the wheelset. Furthermore, in order to reduce P2 forces still further a very simple primary suspension, incorporating steel coil springs was used without friction damping. (figure 2)

(fig 2. LTF25 bogie)

Following this, the principal suspension of the bogie was moved to the secondary position and hour-glass rubber springs were adopted with inclined hydraulic dampers which would not only provide a satisfactory ride, but also would permit the bogie to rotate without the use of the conventional centre pivot and side bearers.

Curving behaviour is a function of primary yaw stiffness and wheel profile, and this together with eliminating the centre pivot and side bearers, which normally have the function of constraining the movement of conventional bogies at high speed, in fact improved the curving performance of the LTF at low speeds, reduced wheel flange contact with the rail to a remarkable extent and these

combine to a further reduction in the potential for noise and wear.

Thus, what we mean by Low Track Force is when the effective load imparted on to the track is lower than that found in conventional freight bogie design. Perhaps, the existing UIC rule 510-2 covering axle load/ wheel diameter relationships could be re-modelled to take this effect into consideration.

We have recognised the UIC standard full in this respect and for all bogies which are to operate other than in the UK, the the wheel diameter / axle load ratio woul conform to the UIC standard, but at th same time would permit an automati increase in the axle load if re-examination of the existing UIC rule were to produce a rational definition o acceptable contact stresses.

3.0 LTF PERFORMANCE.

In August 1991 BR Research made a comparison of track forces from LTF 25 and Y 25 bogies based on earlier experimental and theoretical work. The LTF 25 is designed to operate up to an axle load of 25.5 tonnes and at speeds of up to 120km/h. The Y 25 bogie is designed to operate up to an axle load of 22.5 tonnes, but a similar bogie the FBT6 exists on BR for use on axle loadings up to 25.5 tonnes and this bogie was used in some of the theoretical work, but is limited to 96km/h at this rating.

The site of the bridge was an eight span masonry viaduct situated on a curve so that some lateral force effect would be expected. A variety of measurements were taken at speeds of between 33 - 100km/h. A rake of Y25 vehicles with 22.5 tonne axle load and a single LTF 25 vehicle with 25.5 tonnes was tested.

The conclusion of this test was that even after allowing for the presence of only one LTF 25 vehicle against a rake of Y25 vehicles, the Acceleration Effect Indicator (derived from the measurements of the lateral acceleration of the parapet wall on the outwardly curving side) was only about half that for the Y25 and the report states that this would suggest that the LTF25 at 25.5 tonnes axle load is 'significantly' less damaging in respect of vibration than the Y25 at the lower

22.5 tonnes axle load.

Measurements of the dynamic forces, both vertical and lateral were measured both from the vehicle as well as from the track and figure 3 shows the result of these tests.

These results are for the LTF25 with a 25.5 tonne axle load and the Y25 with the 22.5 tonne axle load and with different wagon bodies.

	Vertical Forces		Lateral Forces	
	Vehicle System	Track System	Masonry Bridge	Steel Bridge
Vehicle Speed (mph)	60	41–47	60	60
Track Standard Deviation (mm)	1.7	1.8	0.6	2.0
LTF25 Dynamic Force (kN)	21–25	22	6	6
Y25 Dynamic Force (kN)	22	23	23	31
Factored force for "25.5 Tonne" Y25	25	26		

(fig 3. LTF25/Y25 track force comparison)

Scaling the Y25 vertical dynamic force results linearly by the difference in axle loads increases the forces to around 25 and 26 kN and this is shown at the base of the table. The lateral forces are very significantly lower for the LTF 25 bogied vehicle.

The BR report titled "Comparison of Track Forces from LTF25 and Y25 Bogies" summarised the findings from the tests and the calculations as follows.

a)   Measurements of acceleration on a masonry bridge suggests that LTF 25 bogies at 25.5 tonne axle load produce about half the acceleration of Y25 bogies at 22.5 tonne axle load. LTF bogies are therefore likely to cause significantly less damage from vibration than Y25s.

b)   Limited measurements of dynamic vertical force show that the LTF 25 at 25.5 tonne axle load produces similar levels of force to the Y25 at 22.5 tonne axle load.

c)   Measurements of lateral force show very significantly lower forces from the LTF 25 bogie than the Y25 bogie.

d)   Calculations of vertical dynamic forces for a range of vehicle conditions show that the LTF 25 bogie almost always produces lower forces than the Y25 bogie. The magnitude of the difference varies with axle load and wagon type.

e)   The difference between the LTF 25 and the Y25 bogies is more significant on smoother track and will be particularly marked on good quality intercity track.

f)   Dynamic forces from LTF 25 bogies are no higher at 120 km/h than at 100 km/h, while the forces from Y25 bogies increase by about 10%

(British Rail do highlight the fact that these results relate to the LTF 25 bogie at 25.5 tonnes and that they can not necessarily be interpolated to the lower axle load bogies.)

4.0   INSIDE BEARINGS AND HOT BOX DETECTION.

The effect of moving the bearings away from the classical outside position has resulted in the conventional trackside hot box detectors used in the UK and the rest of Europe being unable to monitor the temperature of bearings. To overcome this, the LTF bogie is fitted with a fusible plug system of hot box detection which is an onboard passive monitoring system operating continuously whilst the vehicle is in motion.

Each axlebox is fitted with an alloy filled plug which is designed to melt at 97°C. This temperature, measured at the outside of the bearing, corresponds to an internal temperature of approximately 120°C which is below the temperature at which the axlebox grease would degrade. It is also sufficiently early in the failure cycle to enable the wagon to subsequently proceed slowly to a safe stopping point.

The melting of the fusible plug absolutely indicates a rising temperature in the axlebox. There is no need for the axlebox to be touched to establish if it is a spurious alarm. Every hotbox signal should be treated as an indication of a bearing problem, thereby eliminating the necessity for drivers to "exercise discretion" to determine the severity of the cause of the alarm.

The loss of brake air through the fusible plug creates a pressure differential across the emergency exhaust valve, causing it to operate and exhaust train brake air to atmosphere thereby causing emergency brake application bringing the train rapidly to a halt. The whistle valve indicates the location of the faulty hot box and this whistle will continue to blow for as long as the train brake handle is left in the full service position.

It might be of some interest to those attending this Conference that the existing trackside system of hotbox detection is not a matter regulated by the UIC neither is the distance between detectors defined in any degree. Thus an axle bearing which commences to fail after the wagon has just passed a trackside hot box detector detector might have as short a distance as 35 - 40Kms until the next detector appears or it might have over 200Kms to travel.

The two principal advantages of the LTF hot box detection system can be summarised as follows:

(i) It is effective continuously and ....

(ii) ....it only indicates a bearing problem.

These two aspects are singularly absent from the track side systems currently employed which firstly, are intermittent and secondly, do at times sense spurious heat signals from compressors and brakes and are not always able "to see" all bearing box designs, with the result that trains are at times stopped for "false alarms" or indeed are not stopped when they should be.

The only area where the LTF could be seen to conflict with UIC rules is in respect of UIC leaflet 541 which rules against use being made of the main air pipe for other than braking applications. However, since the LTF system makes use of this air pipe in exactly the same way as passenger stock, and indeed makes use of the same emergency exhaust valve, it was conceded by the National Railway Administrations that highlighted this particular clause, that this was unlikely to pose a problem.

5.0 BRAKES

In view of the excellent experience gained by British Rail in the use of wheel mounted disc brakes, we had no concern in adopting such a system on the full range of LTF bogies. On the smaller versions LTF 13 and LTF 14, there is insufficient swept area to mount separate discs and on those sizes the brake pads operate directly on to the wheel surface. On all the larger sizes there are separate brake discs mounted on the wheels, enabling easy replacement as and when they become worn beyond limits.

We commissioned SAB Wabco to conduct simulated tests under all conditions on 640mm wheel diameter wheel set which would carry an axle loading of 14 tonnes under UIC ruling, but if ordered by BR for use in the UK would be offered with an axle loading of 16 tonnes. (figure 4) These tests included simulated runs on the Modane and St Gotthard Passes under both wet and dry conditions and generally conformed to the performance standards required.

(fig 4. LTF 16 bogie)

In our discussions with the various National Railway Administrations, there have been considerable discussions regarding brake disc design and brake pad materials, and at the time of writing there are no revised standards that have yet been defined for disc braked only freight vehicles which would cause us to modify the present braking arrangement.

6. APPROVALS

At the time of writing this report we have had in depth discussions with the many

National Railway Administrations in support of our search for approval of LTF technology in principle:-

SNCF, SNCB, DB, SBB, ÖBB, and the FS.

We have had formal acceptance from the SNCF that wagons fitted with LTF bogies would be accepted on French Railways subject to the wagons having been tested in accordance with UIC rules and subject to the wagons operating in bloc trains, ie in trains of a single wagon type. The DB, the ÖBB and the SNCB have given similar approvals. The SBB has stated that it will follow the lead given by the SNCF and the FS has given similar verbal approval and we await their letter of confirmation.

7.0 BENEFITS.

With its range of 4 models, the LTF covers an axle load span from 13 tonnes at the bottom end (this in effect would be limited to 11 tonnes or thereabouts if the UIC axle load/ wheel diameter rule is applied) in versions at 16 and 18 tonnes up to the LTF 25 with an axle loading of 25.5 tonnes at the top end, (but here again this would be limited to 22.5 tonnes under current UIC rules). We are hopeful that LTF technology will be fully accepted so that the benefit of carrying extra payload at no extra cost can be enjoyed by the operators of such wagons.(figure 5)

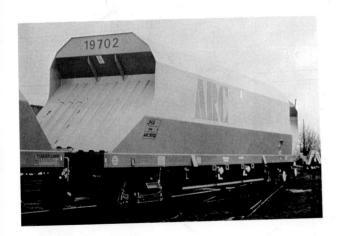

(fig 5. 102 tonne hopper - LTF25 bogies)

At a time when the environment is taking on greater importance, a rail freight vehicle with LTF technology bogies will, in terms of perceived noise, be up to 12db quieter and thus when high speed freight trains are operating at night, the nuisance of noise from conventional bogies can be avoided.

The staff of one UK owner of wagons fitted with LTF bogies have christened it 'the ghost train' because of its quietness resulting from the reduction in both ground and airborne vibration levels.

Flange free curving is attained down to curves of approximately 400m radius. We have measured the wheels of the LTF 25 bogies in service, each of which has completed over 210 000 Kms, and there was no measurable wear either on the tread or on the flanges. We are thus very hesitant in forecasting the effective life between reprofiling, but this might be another area where LTF technology helps the pocket of the operator.

A further benefit arising from the relatively soft secondary lateral suspension is that it gives good lateral stability for a variety of wagon pivot spacings and a combination of axle loadings. This will enable bogie performance to be extended to 140km/h and beyond. For example, the BR Research LTF 25 bogie with 18 tonnes axle load was tested experimentally at speeds up to 160Km/h.

The UK W6a kinematic loading gauge, ie the theoretical space through which a rail vehicle must pass is more constraining than the UIC B gauge which has been widely adopted as the standard loading gauge in Continental Europe. With the lower platform heights available from the LTF bogie range, the opportunity now exists for even larger containers and swop bodies to be carried on BR routes including those that have been modified to the most recent SB1 loading gauge.

Low Track Force technology makes a major contribution to rail freight engineering and as the demand for higher speed freight trains calls for greater freedom of access to train paths that hitherto have been restricted to passenger coaching stock then the inherent advantages of speed and lower track forces that LTF bogies offer will become widely appreciated and accepted.

. . . .

Note:

(1)   Paper published in the Railway Engineering Journal (Railway Division I Mech E) January 1974 "The effect of track and vehicle parameters on wheel/rail vertical dynamic forces" Authors - H H Jenkins, J E Stephenson, G A Clayton, G W Morland and D Lyon.

Acknowledgements:

British Rail Research, for extracts taken from their report dated August 1991. "Comparison of Track Forces from LTF25 and Y25 bogies"

C451/024

Class 92 dual voltage locomotives for Channel Tunnel freight and overnight services

R N MOLE
British Railways Board, Derby

SYNOPSIS

In April 1990 the IMechE held a one day seminar entitled "Channel Tunnel Rolling Stock" and a paper was presented on the Class 92 locomotive. I had been involved in the Class 92 Project only two months at that time and we were drawing towards the end of the evaluation of Tenders.

This paper reviews the developments that have occurred since April 1990 which have had an influence on the locomotive design. I have also taken the opportunity to briefly summarise the history of the Class 92 locomotive beginning from April 1988 and outline the main features of the locomotive design.

1. EXPLANATION OF BACKGROUND

In May 1988 various alternatives to the Class 92 locomotive were under consideration. These included the use of diesel electric locomotives to haul trains between Dollands Moor, at the UK end of the Channel Tunnel, and Wembley.

Options included the purchase of new locomotives designated Class 65 and the use of various combinations of other existing BR locomotives (see Table 1).

Table 1

	To start & move Train Specified i.e. max. 1600 tonnes	To start & move Train at required System Speeds
(a)	1 x Cl 60	2 x Cl 60 (60 mph max)
(b)	2 x Cl 56 or 58	2 x Cl 56 or 58
(c)	2 x Cl 47	3 x Cl 47
(d)	3 x Cl 37/0	4 x Cl 37/0
(e)	2 x Cl 37/7	4 x Cl 37/7

The above options were considered as a direct replacement for a single Class 92 in order to maintain Class 92 transit times on BR routes.

After a long series of appraisals had been made BR concluded that a dual voltage locomotive, for operation on the BR 25KV ac and 750V dc electrified systems and which was also capable of operating through the Channel Tunnel into France (as far as Frethun), was the most cost effective means of providing motive power for hauling trains between Wembley and Frethun.

Providing a locomotive to operate over three railway systems, and which also has to satisfy the stringent safety standards for operating through the Channel Tunnel has proven to be an immense challenge to all the parties who have been involved in the development of the design, particularly the locomotive manufacturer Brush Traction Ltd who has had to fit a large amount of complex equipment into the limited space allowed by the BR loading gauge. The Class 92 will be one of the longest and heaviest electric locomotives ever built for BR.

After commercial and technical evaluation of the offers the Contract was placed with Brush Electrical Machines Limited as Main Contractor, on 22 July 1990 for 20 locomotives. An advantage of the offer from Brush was considered to be the inclusion of ABB and their extensive experience in providing "Tunnelproof" equipment for Swiss Railways. This is most strikingly exemplified by the Simplon tunnel which at 20km in length has extreme winter time conditions viz minus 15^0C outside, plus 40^0C and 100% humidity inside – Railway Authorities in Switzerland specify their equipment to be "Simplonproof".

When the Contract was placed with Brush Electrical Machines Ltd, options for up to another 40 locomotives were available to BR. These were subsequently taken up as three separate tranches for 10, 7 and finally 9 more locomotives making a total of 46 locomotives now ordered.

The 46 locomotives will be maintained by Crewe ETD and operated as a common fleet by Railfreight Distribution acting on behalf of European Passenger Services (EPS) and SNCF. The locomotives will be used mainly for freight haulage between Frethun and Wembley. Haulage of the Channel Tunnel Nightstock coaches will be between Calais Ville and Glasgow/Edinburgh.

Haulage through the Tunnel will be shared between BR and SNCF which necessitates both railways providing electric locomotives suitable for operating in the Tunnel. From this developed the possibility of using a common fleet of Class 92 locomotives for Tunnel haulage which offered benefits to both Railways. Further benefits are possible if single locomotive haulage by a Class 92 locomotive is accepted by the Intergovernmental Safety Commission (IGSC) in the future. The possibility of single locomotive haulage in the Tunnel in the future has been one of the most significant factors influencing the locomotive design.

2. DESCRIPTION OF THE CLASS 92 LOCOMOTIVE

2.1 General

The Class 92 locomotive has a Co–Co wheel arrangement (two 3–axle bogies, all axles powered), it will weigh up to 126 tonnes (route availability RA7) and will be rated at 5.0 MW (6700 hp) when operating from 25kV ac catenary supplies and 4.0 MW (5360 hp) when operating from 750 Vdc third rail supplies to enable the required performances to be achieved when hauling trainloads of upto 1600t. The general arrangement of the locomotive and bogie are shown in Figures 1 and 2.

The maximum design speed was fixed at 140 kph (87 mph), after evaluation of 120 kph and 160 kph options prior to placement of the Contract, this being a compromise based on freight and passenger service requirements. The increase in cost and complexity involved in increasing the speed from 120 kph to 140 kph was relatively small in comparison with increasing the speed up to 160 kph. This would have required a different bogie design with frame mounted traction motors, separate gearboxes and alterations to the bogie suspension on what for the two lower speed options was a bogie based on the Class 60 locomotive bogie design. Interestingly with each speed option a tractive effort (TE) of 400kN was possible with the 3 phase propulsion system without the need for regearing.

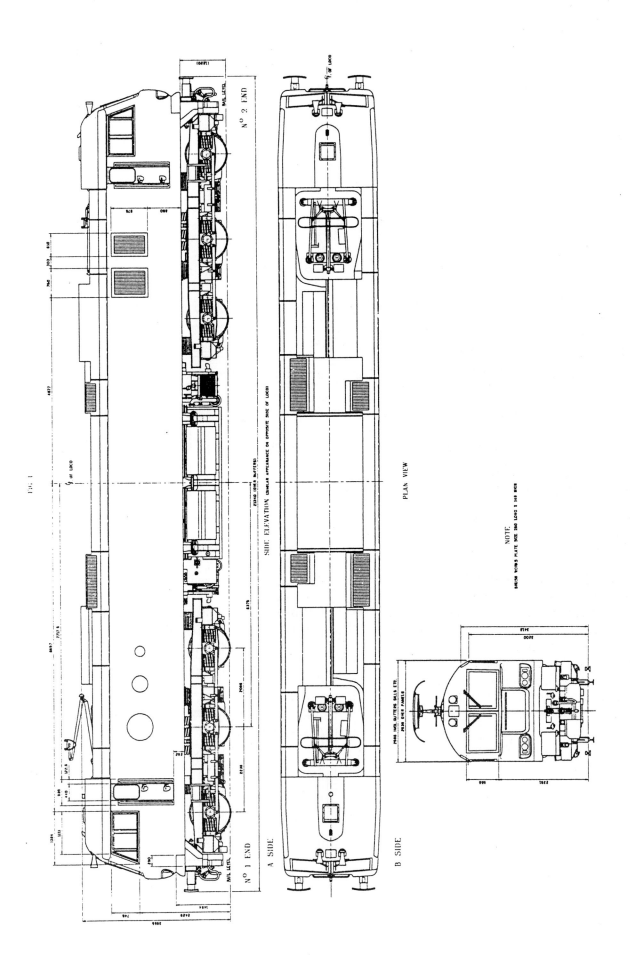

SIDE ELEVATION (SIMILAR APPEARANCE ON OPPOSITE SIDE OF LOCO)

PLAN VIEW

A SIDE

B SIDE

NOTE:
BRUSH WORKS PLATE SIZE 260 LONG X 160 WIDE

Fig 1

Fig 2

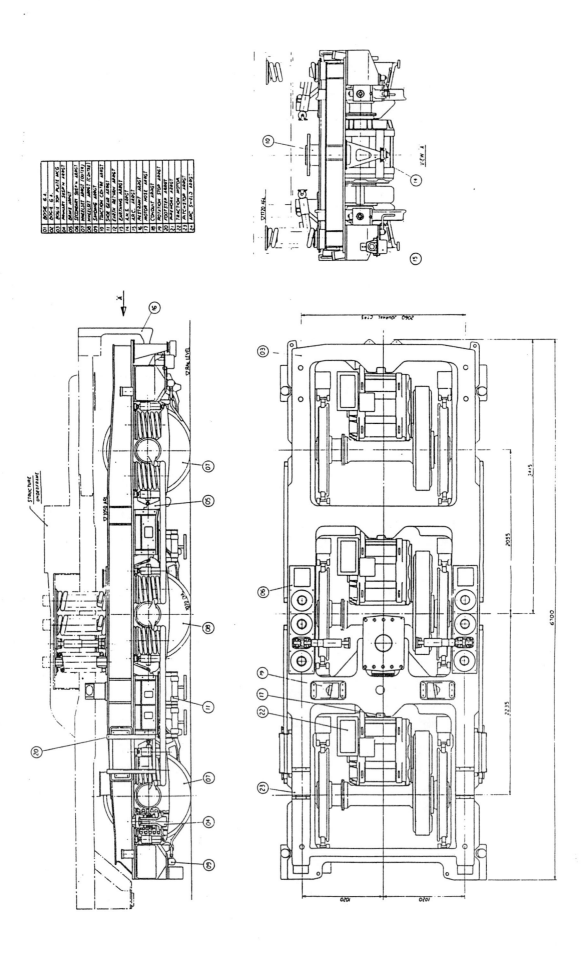

2.1 General (Continued)

Table 2 – Locomotive Overview

DUAL VOLTAGE	25KV ac (BR, SNCF, ET, CTRL*) 750V dc (BR)
CURRENT COLLECTION	ac – Pantogragh(s) dc – 12 shoes (6800A max)
POWER	5 MW 25KV ac 4 MW 750V dc
MAXIMUM TRACTIVE EFFORT	360 KN 400 KN BOOST 200 KN SINGLE BOGIE OPERATIVE
PROPULSION SYSTEM	3 PHASE DRIVE
BRAKING	REGENERATIVE RHEOSTATIC FRICTION
WEIGHT	126 TONNES
ROUTE AVAILABILITY	RA7
OVERALL LENGTH (OVER BUFFERS)	21.340 M
COUPLING	BR STANDARD DRAWHOOK/SCREW COUPLING
CONTROL JUMPERS	61 WAY
ETH JUMPERS	SIMILAR TO BR STANDARD (1500V ac, 750V dc)
ETH INDEX	108 (NIGHTSTOCK) 900KVA, 1500V ac (25KV ac supply) 536KVA, 893V dc (750V dc supply)

* – CTRL = CHANNEL TUNNEL RAIL LINK (To be built in the future).

2.2 Bogie

The bogie is based on existing designs which were used on the Class 60, and Class 89 locomotives. For the Class 92 locomotive the bogie is slightly longer in order to provide additional space between the wheelsets for the shoegear. Between each of the wheelsets is located one of two types of shoe–groups, one has a single shoe and the other two shoes. In total there are three shoes per side for each bogie making a shoegroups total of 12 shoes per locomotive. The shoes are held in the retracted position by spring pressure and are lowered onto the 750Vdc third rail by pressurising a pneumatic cylinder. An indication is provided to the driver of the position of the shoegear.

Automatic Sanders are provided on the outer wheelsets of each bogie, which are isolated when operating in the Channel Tunnel. The wheelsets have hollow axles which helps to reduce the unsprung weight. Other equipment which is mounted on the bogie includes AWS and APC receivers, the DC and AC traction return current brushes and Lifeguards.

2.3 Bodyshell

The bodyshell is made of fabricated steel construction similar to the BR Class 60 locomotive but modified to withstand the higher end–load cases agreed with SNCF and the lifting requirements for re–railing in the Channel Tunnel. The bodyside skin is pre–stressed before being welded on to the body–side pillars in order to give an improved, ripple free finish. The locomotive bodyshell is made up of several subassemblies. The dragboxes, bogie cross stretchers and transformer cross stretcher are welded onto the solebars to make up the underframe. The bodysides which are built up in a jig are then welded onto the underframe. Roof sections and other cab–end sections are then welded onto the main assembley to complete the basic bodyshell structure. The locomotive roof is made up of three sections, each one is removable to enable equipment replacement. The cab roof and cab front are made of pressed steel which are welded onto body structure.

2.4 Driving Cab

The cab design is developed from the BR Railfreight locomotive cab layout though changes to the layout and details have been made to meet the spirit of UIC Fiche 651.

The driver will have a good all round view facing forward and sideways from the seated position. A sliding window will be fitted to each cab side, positioned to enable the driver to lean out and look down the train whilst operating the controls.

Two High Impact Resistant windscreens are provided which are separated vertically. These are designed to withstand the impact from an object travelling at twice the maximum speed of the vehicle. An electrical heating element is fitted as an integral part of the windscreen for demisting. Air operated windscreen wipers are fitted, with washer jets which can be operated independently of the wiper movement.

Two external doors are provided at each cab end for gaining access into the cabs through a transverse vestibule. These have handles at two heights for use at a platform or track level. Inside the vestibule there are two doors for access to the cab and equipment compartment. The cab layout, doorway sizes, and direction of opening of the doorways are designed to allow the driver to exit the cab quickly in an emergency and to seek shelter in a "refuge" within the equipment compartment.

2.4.1 Air Conditioning System

The cab air conditioning system allows the driver to regulate the cab temperature between 18^0C and 26^0C and is designed to cater for external ambient temperatures of down to -30^0C under which conditions the cab temperature will be maintained at 18^0C or more. The system will also maintain a cab interior temperature of 21^0C and an interior relative humidity of 50% in external ambient conditions of 28^0C, 45% relative humidity. The system is also capable of supplying fresh and recirculated air dependent on the external ambient temperature.

The fresh air intake will automatically close when the fire detection equipment is operated within the locomotive. This is intended to prevent fumes being introduced into the cab.

The ventilation fans will continue to run in the event of an interruption of the 25KV ac power supply for at least 30 minutes after which the fan will be switched off automatically to preserve battery capacity.

2.4.2 Cab Noise Levels

The cab design ensures that the noise levels within the locomotive are kept to a minimum. The average sound level measured over a typical journey (LA(EQ)J should not exceed 82dBA using BR measurement methods, and 80dBA, over 3 return journeys portal to portal in the Tunnel using UIC Fiche 651 measurement methods.

2.4.3 Controls

The ergonimically designed cab interior layout provides easy access to the seating positions, the majority of the controls and switches being positioned towards the left hand side of the cab. The main driving instruments, gauges, switches, warning lights, cab signalling equipment, and brake controllers are positioned in front and to the left of the driver. To the driver's right hand side is positioned the master controller, incorporating the direction selector and power controller, which is mounted on a pedestal (see illustrations Figures 3 and 4).

The direction of operation of the brake controllers and power controller conforms to UIC practice which is opposite to the normal BR practice. To ensure BR drivers are reminded of this the shape/colour of the controller handles will be different to those on other BR locomotives.

Where there is sufficient space available on the cab desk the functions of the controls will be denoted by pictograms to UIC standards.

Some interesting features worth noting are (see Figure 5):–

a) The diagnostic annunciator screen (item 50) to the front and left of the seated driver which can be used by the driver to check the status of the locomotive The diagnostic system is capable of displaying three levels of information. Level 1 is for the use of the driver, Level 2 is intended to be used by maintenance staff and Level 3 forms a comprehensive database of the locomotive performance over a given period of time. A switch is provided to enable the information to be displayed in French or English.

b) The 4–position system selector switch, to the front of the driver (item 12) is for selection of the relevant supply system viz BR 25 KV ac overhead, BR 750V dc third rail or ET 25 KV ac overhead, the fourth position will be used for the new line between London and the Channel Tunnel when it is completed in the future. The locomotive speed is indicated in mph or kph depending on the position of this switch.

c) The TVM 430 cab signalling, speed displays (item 04) which indicate to the driver the speed restrictions when operating within the Tunnel. The second of the two displays is a back–up.

d) Item 9 is the "International Radio" which combines the standard BR radio and the European UIC radio.

e) Item 3 enables the driver to select a particular speed by the adjustment of a rotary speed–set control. A digital indication of the speed which has been set by the driver is provided. Once the locomotive has reached the set–speed the control system will maintain the locomotive speed with $\pm$ 5kph.

2.5 Electrical Equipment

An ABB 3 phase, asynchronous traction propulsion system is provided which is based on ABB three phase propulsion systems in use on several classes of locomotive already in service in Europe. The Class 92 three phase propulsion equipment is similar to that being used on the Eurotunnel Shuttle locomotives, which are also being supplied by Brush Traction Ltd, and is a development of the propulsion equipments being provided by ABB for the Austrian Federal Railways Class 1822 dual voltage locomotive (Brenner locomotive 4.4MW, 140kph, 280KN max TE), and the Swiss Federal Railways locomotive 2000 (6.1MW, 230kph, 270KN max TE). Both of these locomotives are currently being delivered.

The Class 92 Locomotive control system makes extensive use of microprocessors which can be pre–programmed and easily modified if required. The locomotive control systems are connected to the power and auxiliary systems via input and output modules which communicate using an optical–fibre databus.

When operating in the Tunnel the locomotive is provided with automatic train protection (ATP) that will automatically apply the train brakes if the driver exceeds the maximum line speeds for the train braking performance, and the on–board equipment is compatible with the infrastructure provided within the Tunnel. The system which has been selected by Eurotunnel is the TVM 430 signalling system which incorporates, in addition to the automatic train protection feature, a cab signalling display. It also controls the automatic opening and reclosing of the locomotive main circuit breaker during the transition of the overhead catenary neutral sections.

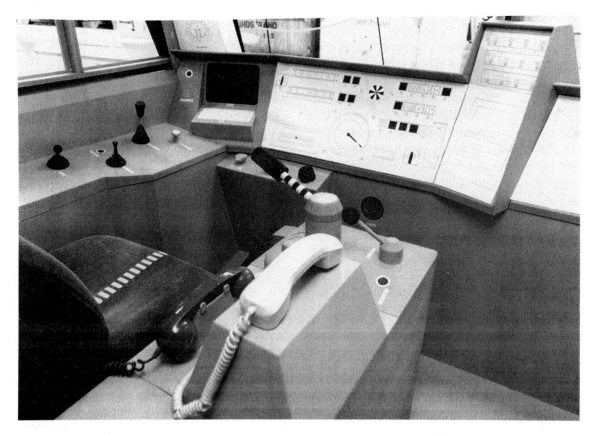

Class 92 Cab Mock – Up

Fig 3

Class 92 Cab Mock – Up

Fig 4

Drivers Instruments Panel

Fig 5

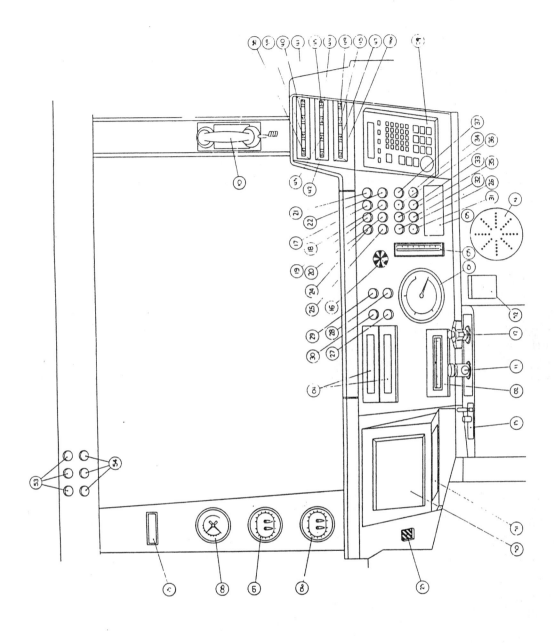

REF	DESCRIPTION
01	BRAKE PIPE PRESSURE GAUGE
02	SPEEDOMETER
03	SPEED SET CONTROL & INDICATOR
04	TVM 430 DISPLAY UNIT
05	TRACTIVE BRAKE EFFORT METER
06	BRAKE CYLINDER GAUGE
07	MAIN RESERVOIR GAUGE
08	AIR FLOW GAUGE
09	INTERNATIONAL TRAIN RADIO
10	INTERNATIONAL TRAIN RADIO H/SET
11	POWER ENABLE CONTROL
12	SYSTEM SELECTOR
13	WINDSCREEN WASH WIPE
14	TONE GENERATOR LOUDSPEAKER
15	DIGITAL CLOCK
16	AWS DISPLAY
17	LINE SUPPLY INDICATOR - MASTER
18	LINE SUPPLY INDICATOR - SLAVE
19	VCB1-HSCB OPEN INDICATOR - MAST
20	VCB/HSCB OPEN INDICATOR - SLV
21	APC CONTROL INDICATOR - MASTER
22	APC CONTROL INDICATOR - SLAVE
23	PARKING BRAKE INDICATOR
24	AWS ENERGISE
25	AWS DISPLAY BLANKING
26	VCB/HSCB OPEN TRIP (GREEN)
27	TVM 430 ARM EVEN No2 (BLACK)
28	TVM 430 ARM ODD No1 (BLACK)
29	TVM 430 DISARM (BLACK)
30	TVM 430 PASS STOP SIGNAL (BLACK)
31	ETS SET
32	ETS TRIP
33	PASS COACH ALARM
34	BATTERY DISCHARGE RESET
35	CLOSE AIR CON DAMPERS
36	SIGNAL BELL
37	HAZARD WARNING LIGHTS
38	GENERAL FAULT LED
39	SAFETY SYSTEM ISOLATED LED
40	FIRE SYSTEM LED
41	OTMR FAILED LED
42	EP ASSIST LED
43	BRAKE CONTINUITY TEST
44	WHEELSLIP LED
45	AUTOSAND LED
46	LIGHTS FAILED LED
47	DOORS CLOSED AND BLOCK
48	TVM 430 PACKAGE ISOLATED LED
49	ET ATP LED
50	ANNUNCIATOR
51	KEYPAD
52	ASH TRAY
53	FIRE WARNING LAMP/ FIRE SYSTEM
54	FIRE SYSTEM OPERATE P/B (BLACK)

2.5   Electrical Equipment (Continued)

Class 92 locomotives will be able to operate in multiple control, either in close multiple or remote multiple (front and rear of passenger trains fitted with through cabling). A maximum of two locomotives can be operated in multiple control. Signals are transmitted between locomotives using a two wire, time division multiplex (TDM) system plus a small number of hardwired signals for certain safety–critical functions. The ability to operate locomotives in multiple control will only be used within the Channel Tunnel between Dollands Moor and Frethun/Calais Ville.

2.6   Power Circuit

The power circuit arrangement shown in Fig 6 is made up of two identical propulsion packages, one for each bogie, consisting of a 4–quadrant controller, which also functions as a step–up chopper on 750V dc supplies, a DC link and three phase invertor which supplies the three asynchronous traction motors with a variable frequency and voltage supply.

When operating on 25KV ac supply systems current is collected from the overhead line by one of two pantographs, normally the trailing pantograph. It is then fed via the vacuum circuit breaker to the main transformer primary winding. The traction return current flows back to the power supply through axle end return brushes which are provided on the ends of 4 axles. Secondary windings on the main transformer supply each of the bogie propulsion packages. A tertiary winding is provided to supply the Electric Train Supplies at 1500V ac.

When operating on 750V dc supply systems current is collected from the third rail by the shoes. The shoes are arranged in two identical circuits in order to keep the traction current to manageable proportions (3,400A max per circuit). The current in each part of the circuit is continuously monitored by current transformers to detect when the locomotive is "gapping" in order to initiate, under certain conditions, a reduction in current prior to the last shoe leaving the conductor rail thereby reducing the arc–energy. The 750V dc supply voltage is conditioned by a step–up chopper to supply the dc link.

The traction return current returns to the running rail through its own return circuit and brush gear which are provided on each traction motor suspension tube. The Electric Train Supply is fed from the locomotive at 750V dc third rail supply voltage.

Contactors between the transformer secondaries and the dc supply ensure that only one of the supply sources can be connected at a time. The pantograph(s) are isolated and earthed whilst the shoegear is operative and vice versa.

The changeover from one supply system to another is carried out by the driver who uses the Power Enable and System Selector switches.

It is possible whilst operating on 25KV ac supply systems to automatically changeover from the operative to the non–operative pantograph without stopping the locomotive. This feature is provided to maximise the ability of the locomotive to continue without stopping in the Tunnel should a pantograph failure occur. Following extensive reliability studies by BR it was concluded that for the majority of pantograph failures the provision of a second pantograph would enable the locomotive to continue in service thereby increasing the reliability (see Fig 7 for arrangement of roof equipment).

An arrangement of isolating and earthing switches, which are interlocked with each other, are provided to isolate the locomotive safely for maintenance work to be carried out.

Fig 6

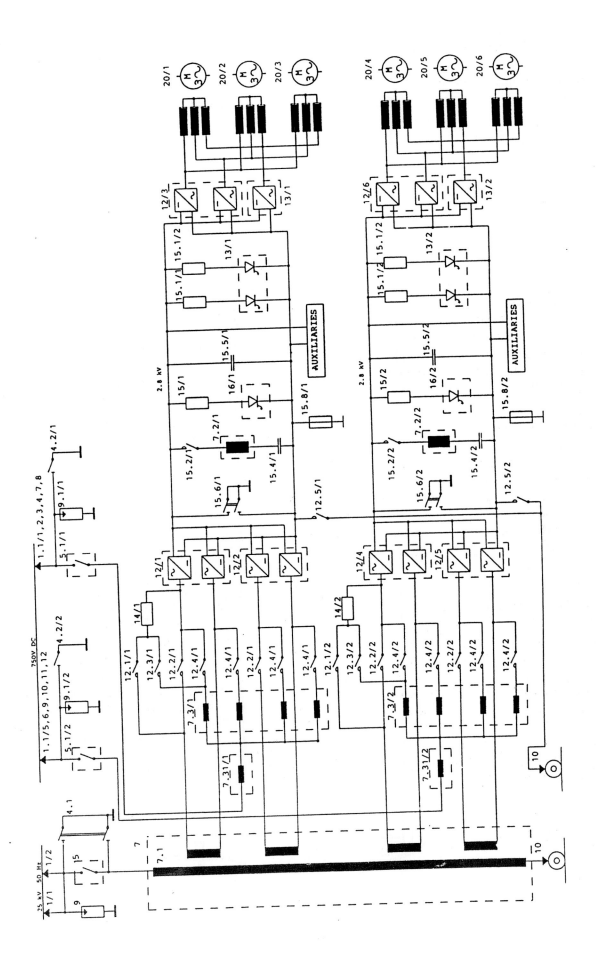

Fig 7

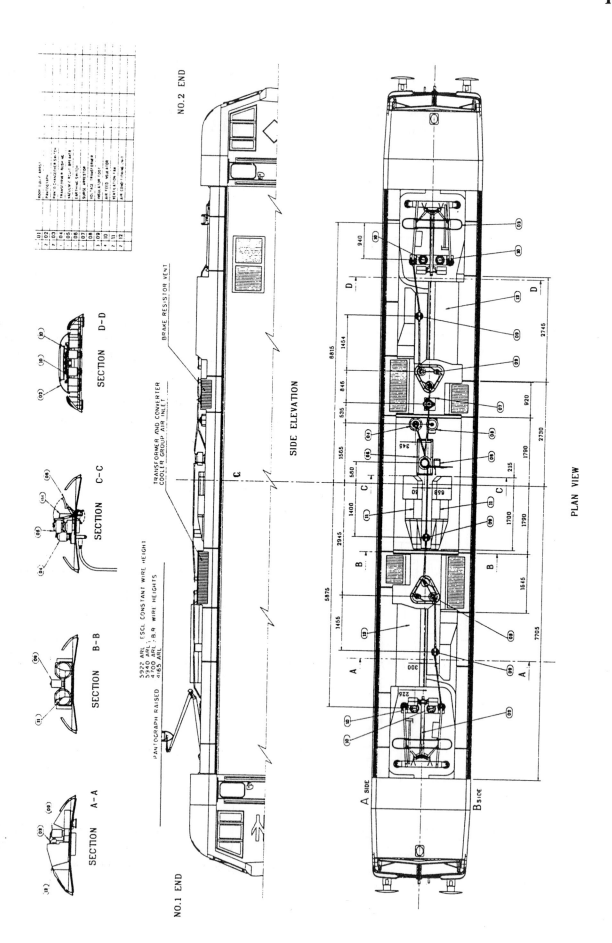

NO.2 END

SECTION D-D

SECTION C-C

SECTION B-B

SECTION A-A

NO.1 END

SIDE ELEVATION

PLAN VIEW

BRAKE RESISTOR VENT

TRANSFORMER AND CONVERTER
COOLER GROUP AIR INLET

PANTOGRAPH RAISED

5922 ARL ESCL CONSTANT WIRE HEIGHT
5940 ARL
4700 ARL: B.R WIRE HEIGHTS
4165 ARL

© IMechE 1992 C451/024

2.7 Auxiliary Circuit

The Auxiliary Circuit is duplicated in a similar manner to the power circuit to ensure that the failure of equipment required for the operation of one bogie propulsion package does not affect the continued operation of the remaining bogie package. Each auxiliary supply, each one being taken from the DC link, supplies an oil cooler blower, traction motor blower, cab air conditioning unit, dynamic brake blower motor, compressor motor, transformer oil pump, convertor oil pump and body ventilation fans. Equipment which is not duplicated such as the battery charger can be fed from either auxiliary supply to ensure that isolation of a bogie package does not prevent the non–duplicated equipment from operating.

2.8 Communications Equipment (See Fig 8)

Radio equipment is provided which is compatible with the radio ground stations provided by Eurotunnel within the Tunnel. The radio for communicating between the locomotive and ground station will be based on the standard BR track to train radio and will also be suitable for use in France.

A portable "Concession" Radio will also be provided in each cab for use by the driver in the Tunnel as a back–up to the main radio described above.

A BR National Radio Network (NRN) radio will also be provided in each cab for use in the UK.

Communications between all driving cabs of all locomotives will be possible wherever the electrical connections between the locomotives and train (in the case of passenger trains) are connected.

Communications between the driver and the train manager of the passenger train are also provided.

2.9 Air Supply System

Each locomotive has two identical motor/compressor sets mounted under the locomotive on flexible suspension mounts.

Air supplied to the locomotive systems should be virtually oil and moisture free. Oil will be removed by a filter before the moisture is taken out of the air by the air dryer. Operation of the compressors is controlled by pressure governors set to close at 9 bar Main Reservoir pressure falling and open at 10 bar Main Reservoir pressure rising.

A low Main Reservoir Governor provides air supply protection by initiating a brake application if the reservoir pressure falls below 4.5 bar.

2.10 Braking System

The brake system comprises an electrically controlled automatic air brake, which includes equipment to allow blending with the electrical dynamic brake, and an independent straight air brake. Within the Tunnel the dynamic braking is carried out regeneratively, and elsewhere it will be rheostatic. Both types of dynamic brake are blended with the friction brake.

Fig 8

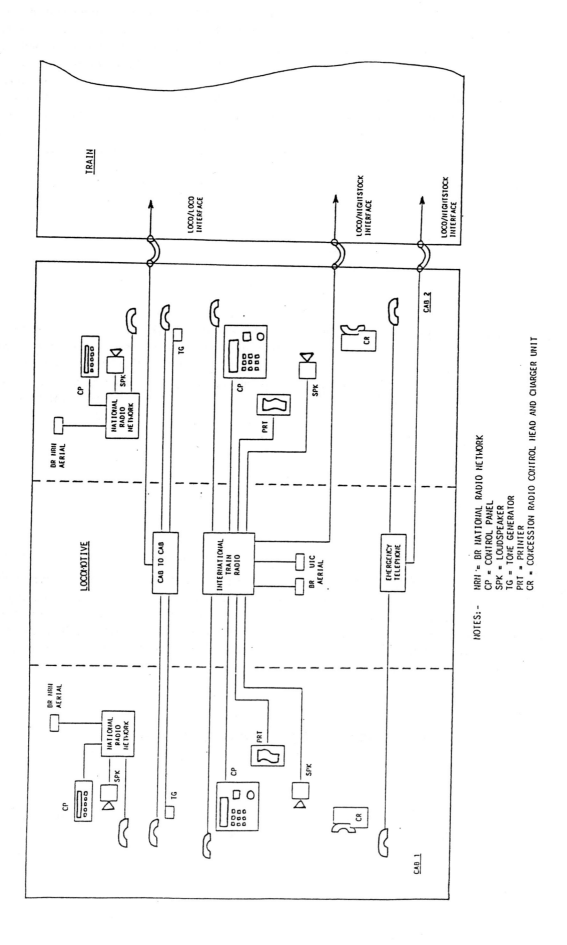

NOTES:- NRN = BR NATIONAL RADIO NETWORK
CP = CONTROL PANEL
SPK = LOUDSPEAKER
TG = TONE GENERATOR
PRT = PRINTER
CR = CONCESSION RADIO CONTROL HEAD AND CHARGER UNIT

2.10.1 Automatic Air Brake

The automatic air brake used on the locomotive is similar to that currently used on other modern BR locomotives and is the "PBL" type. This controls the brake application force by varying the pressure in the brake pipe. The brake pipe is charged to 5 bar to release the brakes and is reduced to apply the brakes. Each vehicle is fitted with a distributor which operates to apply or release the air brake, in proportion to the change in brake pipe pressure on that particular vehicle.

Normal control of the brake pipe is by the driver's brake controller in each cab. The controller is of a joystick type and produces electrical output signals to the brake pipe control unit, which then adjusts the brake pipe pressure accordingly. The length of time the controller is held in the apply or release position determines the level of change in the brake pipe pressure and brake force being applied. There is a separate brake cylinder pressure control system for each bogie which comprises distributors, relay valves, brake supply reservoirs etc. The systems are identical and operate in unison but independently of each other.

2.10.2 Straight Air Brake

The locomotive also contains a normal straight air brake providing a means of applying and releasing the brakes on the locomotive independently of the train brake. If a straight air brake application takes place the dynamic brake, if present, is removed automatically to ensure compounding of dynamic and friction brakes does not occur.

The driver's straight air brake valve can be used to control the automatic air brake if necessary. This is undertaken by moving a Changeover valve from the "Normal" to "Emergency" position, allowing the apply and release ports of the straight air brake valve to connect directly to the equalising reservoir.

2.10.3 Dynamic Brake

Even though the friction brake is the primary safety brake, dynamic braking (Regenerative or Rheostatic) will be used preferentially in normal braking service. The friction brake will make up for any shortfall in the dynamic brake and will always be applied before the locomotive comes to a standstill. A continuous blending system is used to ensure this takes place within jerk rate limitations. If the dynamic brake is lost on one bogie, the friction brake will make up for the loss on that bogie, such that the total level of braking is the same on both bogies (See Fig 9 for electrical braking performance).

Fig 10

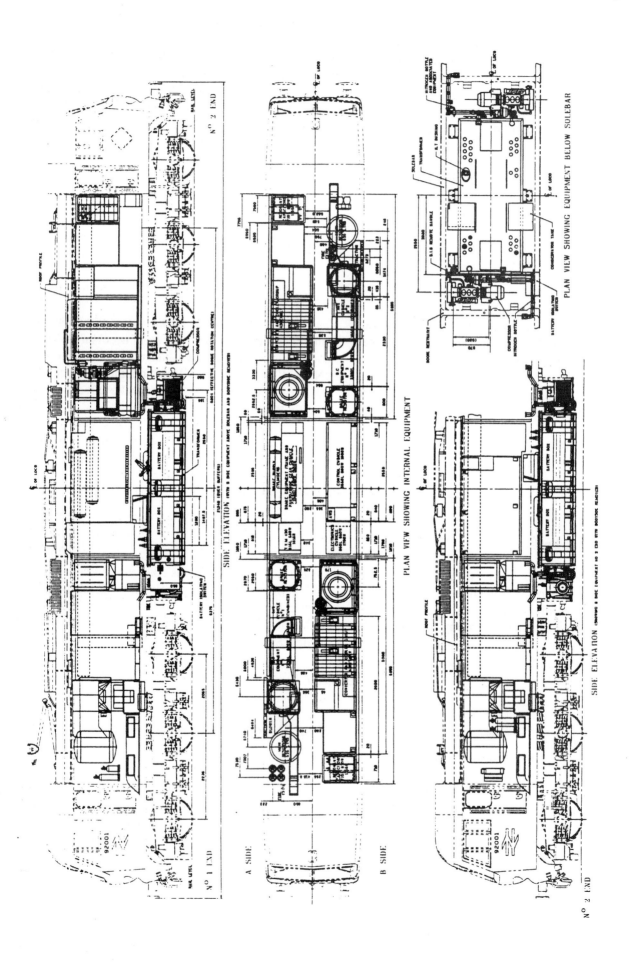

PLAN VIEW SHOWING EQUIPMENT BELOW SOLEBAR

SIDE ELEVATION

PLAN VIEW SHOWING INTERNAL EQUIPMENT

SIDE ELEVATION

2.11 Intervehicle Connections

Each end of the locomotive will be provided with BR standard drawgear and screw couplings together with hydraulic buffers. Air connections will consist of two main reservoir pipe connections and two brake pipe connections. This will provide compatibility with both BR and international rolling stock, including ET and SNCF locomotives, which follow UIC standards for buffering and coupling and facilitate emergency rescue within the Channel Tunnel, France and Britain.

The electrical connections will be non–standard and suitable only for coupling Class 92 locomotive to Class 92 locomotive, and Class 92 locomotive to Channel Tunnel Nightstock Passenger Trains. These connections consist of electric train supply connectors and 61 way bifurcated control connections.

3. SPECIAL CONDITIONS

The underlying design philosophy for the Class 92 locomotive has been to maximise the ability of the locomotive to continue operating under various failure scenarios e.g. failure of a traction propulsion package, pantograph failure, fire within the Channel Tunnel.

One of the most fundamental concepts employed is that of "zoning" the locomotive into 3 distinct zones, two traction zones and a common zone.

Each zone is independently protected by separate detection and extinguishing equipment to allow identification, isolation and discharge of extinguishant into only the affected zone.

The fire protection system comprises two separate systems, a main electrically controlled zoned automatic system, and a reserve mechanically controlled non–zoned system.

The selection of materials and test methods for determining their suitability against specific criteria will be in accordance with BS 6853:1987. "Fire precautions in the design and construction of railway passenger stock" augmented by British Railways Board Code of Practice CP–DDE–101 Issue F.

Since the traction propulsion system is duplicated for each bogie it has been possible to install all the equipment associated with each bogie into separate traction zones. Figure 10 shows the locomotive equipment layout. In each traction zone there is the traction motor blower, converter and cooler group assembly, resonant capacitors, brake resistor and DC equipment and Auxiliary Cubicles. The two traction zones are virtually mirror images of each other. The two traction zones are considered to be the primary risk areas

for the occurrence of fire and consequently are each enclosed within two fire bulkheads each rated for 30 minutes to prevent the spread of fire. Equipment within the central, common zone is equipment which is generally not duplicated and which is essential for the operation of the locomotive. This includes the brake frame, locomotive control electronics cubicle, control equipment cubicle, and the TVM430 cubicle. The TVM430 equipment purchased from CSEE transport Ltd provides cab signalling, automatic train protection, and automatic power control when operating in the Channel Tunnel. Equipment within this zone is generally low voltage with consequently low fire risk.

Services which pass through the traction zones are protected from the effects of a fire occurring within these zones by special measures. Brake system pipework and electrical cabling that is vital for the continued operation of the locomotive should a fire occur and continue unchecked in a traction zone is protected by special fireproof trunking. In the case of pipework the material chosen is stainless steel (see Fig 11).

To complement the zoning of the equipment in this way, an advanced fire protection system is provided, capable of detecting and extinguishing a fire in all above–floor areas of the locomotive with the exception of the driving cabs and vestibules, which are protected by portable extinguishers.

The detection of overheat and/or fire in each zone is accomplished by detectors which are strategically positioned within the zones and are wired in a dual loop configuration with two detectors mounted closely together as a dual–detection pair. This enables two levels of detection – FIRE and FAULT.

Fig 11

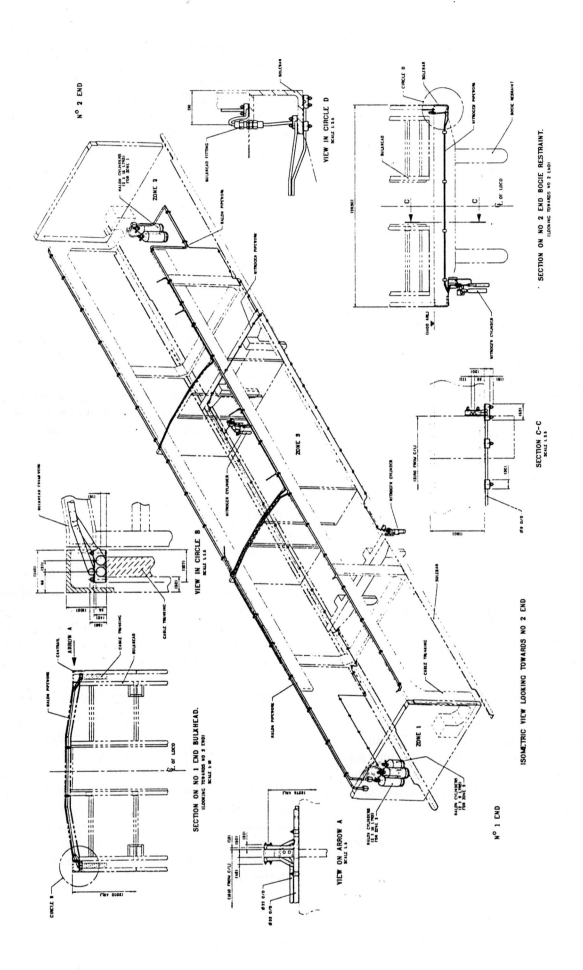

3. SPECIAL CONDITIONS (Continued)

Detection of a fire in any one or more of the zones will cause an audible bell to sound in all drivers cabs. The driver will be informed through the annunciator in which zone fire has been detected. The driver can then delay the automatic discharge of the extinguishant, dependant upon which zone is indicated and the circumstances prevailing. When two locomotives are operating in multiple control (remote or close multiple) the non driving, or slave, locomotive's fire detection system will operate immediately and cannot be delayed by the driver.

When fire is detected in a traction zone and the driver does not delay operation of the extinguishant system the vacuum circuit breaker (VCB) will open, the relevant traction zone equipment will be automatically isolated, and the VCB will reclose restoring power to the remaining healthy traction equipment. The extinguishant will then be released in the traction zone where the fire was detected, extinguishant released into the general area and individual cubicles. The duplication of the electrical equipment, coupled with the physical installation of this equipment in zones in this way, enables the sophisticated fire protection system to be most effective. It also means the Class 92 locomotive could almost be considered to be two locomotives in one!

These are likely to become vital factors as both BR and SNCF seek agreement of the IGSC to single locomotive operation of freight trains up to approximately 1300t through the Channel Tunnel. The 1300t limit has been determined from the theoretical performance capability of the locomotive with only a single bogie propulsion package operating and will be subject to trials within the Channel Tunnel to verify the train load, ie, the ability to restart the locomotive on the worst gradients in the Tunnel with only bogie propulsion package operative.

To complement this ultimate objective the second pantograph on the locomotive is designed so that in the event of the first pantograph developing a fault it can be raised at speed without stopping the locomotive.

It has been calculated that a locomotive with only a single bogie propulsion package operating could haul a 1600t freight train through the Channel Tunnel provided it did not have to stop. The ability to change over pantographs at speed, together with the zoning and other design features, maximises this possibility.

Reliability studies are currently being carried out and it is expected that the results will further demonstrate the suitability of a single locomotive to haul 1300t/1600t trains through the Channel Tunnel.

4. PERFORMANCE

The following principal __normal__ performance requirements were set for the Class 92 locomotive.

a) Hauling 1600 tonne trains on the BR 750V dc supply system between Willesden and Dollands Moor via Tonbridge and Redhill utilising train and service data provided by BR on timing data and speed restrictions, route gradients etc.

b) Hauling 1600 tonne trains between Dollands Moor and Beussingue Portal on the 25 kV ac supply through the Channel Tunnel utilising train and service data provided by BR on timing data and speed restrictions, route gradients etc.

c) For rating purposes the locomotive will be capable of hauling 1600 tonne trains on the BR 25KV ac supply system between Glasgow and Carlisle via Beattock, utilising train and service data provided by BR on timing data and speed restrictions, route gradients etc. In addition, the following emergency performance requirements were set:-

a) The locomotive will be capable of starting and hauling a train of 1600 tonnes from Beattock to Beattock Summit without damage to the electrical equipment utilising train and service data provided by BR on timing data and speed restrictions, route gradients etc.

4. PERFORMANCE (Continued)

b) On isolated occasions, the locomotive shall be capable of starting and hauling a train of 1600 tonnes plus a dead locomotive of the same type from kilometre 23, up the gradient to Castle Hill portal without damage to the electrical equipment, utilising the train and service data provided by BR. This emergency duty shall be achieved under full power and at a restricted speed of 30kph for emergency evacuation.

c) In an emergency there is a need to work trains of various loads at up to 2200 tonnes from any position within the Channel Tunnel to the exit at a speed of 30kph.

A tractive effort (TE) of at least 380kN was originally specified by BR. Although a 400kN capability is available for the Class 92 locomotive this is now only provided as a "boost" facility.

International Freight Rolling Stock drawbar strength limitations meant that for normal operation the total tractive effort needed to be limited to 360kN either for a single locomotive or two locomotives working in close multiple control. The TE applied by each operative bogie propulsion package is shared equally between the operative packages so utilising the available adhesions as effectively as possible. Exceptions to these rules are:

a) When two locomotives are operating in remote multiple control in which case each one is capable of providing a TE of 360kN.

b) When a single locomotive is hauling a train the loss of one bogie propulsion package would automatically enable the remaining package to provide a TE of 200kN. This is calculated, subject to the adhesion which is available, to enable a train of approximately 1300t to be restarted within the Tunnel.

The characteristics of TE against speed are shown in Fig 12.

5. CONCLUSION

The class 92 locomotive is an important part of BR and SNCF's strategy for the haulage of freight trains and Channel Tunnel Nightstock Passenger Trains through the Channel Tunnel.

The design of the locomotive has been developed to ensure the aspirations of both Railways can be achieved. Of special significance is the zoning and duplication of equipment which it is hoped will enable single locomotive haulage of freight trains through the Channel Tunnel in the future.

6. ACKNOWLEDGEMENTS

The author wishes to thank British Railways (Railfreight Distribution and European Passenger Services), SNCF, and Brush Traction for their kind permission to publish this paper; and to express his appreciation for the assistance given.

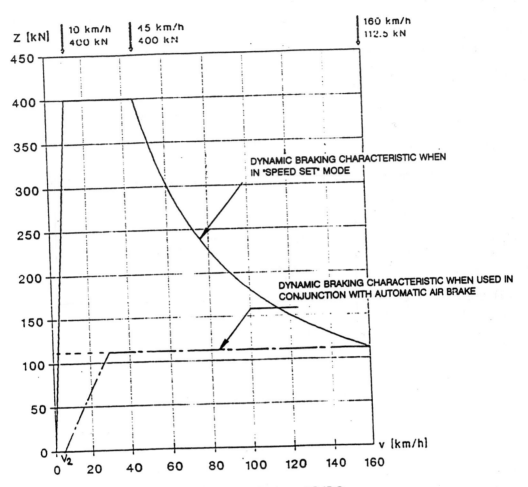

Fig 9

Fig 12

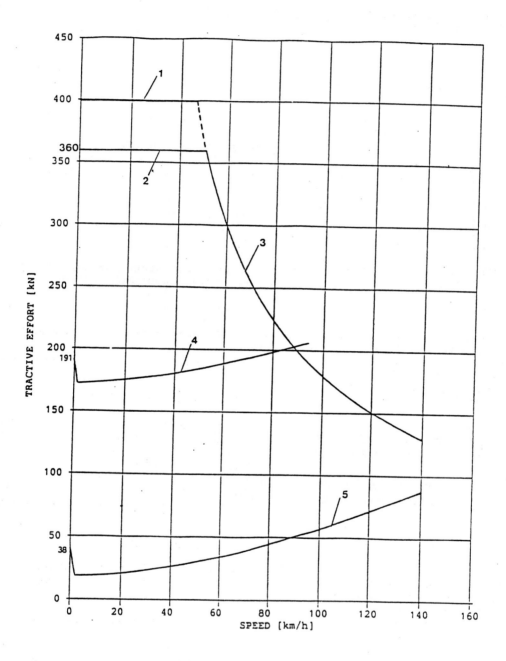

1   Design maximum tractive effort of 400kN.

2   Maximum in service tractive effort/speed characteristic.

3   Maximum rail power of 5.0MW.

4   Running resistance curve for one Class 92 hauling 1300 tonnes through the tunnel up a rising gradient of 1.1%.

5   Running resistance curve for one Class 92 hauling 1300 tonnes through the tunnel on level track.

C451/018

Quality management for the design and manufacturing of the Channel Tunnel rolling stocks

L VU HONG, MASQC and D MONTALT
Transmanche Link, Folkestone, Kent

SYNOPSIS The specificity of the Channel Tunnel Rolling Stock requires the implementation of stringent QA requirements during design and manufacturing phases. Formal Design Review, Prototype Tests, First Article Inspection are the main features which have been developed and implemented.

1   INTRODUCTION

The Channel Tunnel project is an entirely original project, both from the point of view of the concept itself (organising the transport of vehicles under the Channel by means of a rail facility), and from the point of view of the complex organisation set up.

Whereas standard rail transport systems usually bring together an operator and a constructor, the Channel Tunnel is a multi-disciplinary project, which involves many organisations interfacing with each other (see Appendix 1).

- IGC   The Inter-Governmental Commission, which gives the operating licence and sets the safety regulations.

- ET   Eurotunnel, the operator

- MdO   The Maître d'Oeuvre

- TML   The constructor, a consortium of 10 major French and British companies.

- Manufacturers
Responsible for providing the design, manufacture, installation and commissioning of fixed equipment and rolling stock.

- SNCF/BR/SNCB
As users of the tunnel.

Added to this organisational complexity, there are time and budgetary restrictions, given that this is a private project which must be profitable for all those involved.

2   SHUTTLE ROLLING STOCK

The rolling stock is one of the components of the Channel Tunnel, and will be exceptional in its characteristics and in its performances.

The wagons will have unusual dimensions, with a width of 4.1 m and a height above the rail of 5.6 m.

Rolling Stock orders can be summarised as follows:-

- Electric locomotives   38
- Diesel locomotives   5
- Tourist wagons   254
- Heavy good wagons   270

The wagon orders break down as follows:-

- Tourist Wagons (for transporting cars and coaches):-

SDC	(Single Deck Carrier)	108
SDL	(Single Deck Loader)	19
DDC	(Double Deck Carrier)	108
DDL	(Double Deck Loader)	19
Total tourist wagons		254

They can make up to 9 trains, each capable of transporting up to 240 cars for a homogenous shuttle of DDC wagons.

- Heavy Goods Wagons

HGVC	(Heavy Goods Vehicle Carrier)	228
HGVL	(Heavy Goods Vehicle Loader)	33
AMC	(Amenity Coach)	9
Total Heavy Goods Wagons		270

They can make up to 8 trains, each capable of transporting 28 Heavy Goods Vehicles of 44 tonnes each.

These shuttle trains, composed of carrier wagons, loader wagons and two locomotives (one at each end for safety reasons), will be up to 776m long and will weight up to 2,300 tonnes.

This load will be pulled by a fleet of 38 locomotives weighing 130 tonnes and having 3 bogies with two motor axles, providing a tractive power of 5.6 MW.

They will be used to carry out a journey from terminal to terminal in about 35 minutes.

The development of the rolling stock must also take into consideration many parameters which are specific to the unique environment of this project:-

- Aerodynamics in the tunnel (piston effect) and in the terminals (the effect of cross-winds during a storm on high rolling stock),

- Safety: the non-segregation of occupants from tourist vehicles leads to unusual fire protection systems (detection and extinguishing),

- Reliability and maintainability of the equipment (the project must be economically viable),

- Compatibility with fixed equipment in the tunnel and with terminal structures,

- Compatibility with other rolling stock (the TMST, i.e. the Transmanche Super Train, and freight trains),

- Passenger comfort: since the system will be competing with other means of transport such as aeroplanes, ferries, catamarans, the service offered must be good enough to induce consumers to use the Tunnel again.

Faced with requirements of this level, quality management of the highest order is vital. The Quality Assurance level is set at the highest standard in this field. The standards used are ISO 9001 or BS 5750 Part 1.

TML has therefore made arrangements to provide this level of quality to design, manufacture, installation and commissioning, and has therefore developed a system specific to this project.

This system is described in the Quality Assurance Manual, which contains a programme defining TML's QA policy, and which is wholly supported by the Management. There is also a set of procedures and organisation manuals supporting this programme.

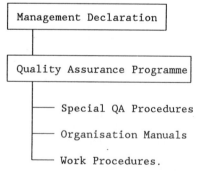

These QA requirements are passed on to suppliers via a set of QA specifications, which can be modified according to the type of activity and its level of importance.

	Level 1	Level 2	Level 3	Unclassified
Design	D1	D2	D3	No requirement
Manufacture	M1	M2a/M2b	M3	"
Installation	C1	C2	C3	"

Rolling stock was ordered at level 1, comprising all the requirements of ISO 9001 or BS 5750 Part 1.

3 ORGANISATION

Orders have been placed with several organisations/consortia located in various countries (see Appendix 2):-

Equipment	Manufacturer	Factories
Electric locomotives	ESCL Consortium (Euroshuttle Locos)	BRUSH (Loughborough) mechanical ABB (Zurich - Geneva) electrical
Tourist Wagons	ESCW Consortium (Euroshuttle Wagons)	BOMBARDIER (La Pocatière) DDL + kits of the wagon car bodies ANF (Crespin) DDC BN (Bruges) SDC FIAT (Savigliano) SDL
Heavy Goods Wagons	Breda Fiat Consortium	FIAT (Savigliano) + bogies BREDA (Pistoia) IMESI (Palermo) OMECA (Reggio Calabria) FERROSUD (Matera)

4 DESIGN QUALITY

Although railway equipment is subject to a very high degree of standardisation by the UIC, the original nature of the Channel Tunnel Rolling Stock involves a new design. Therefore, very special attention has been paid to design quality.

Four lines of design verification have been defined to validate designs:-

- Formal design review,
- Prototype,
- Type test,
- Routine verifications.

4.1 Routine Design Verifications

Rigorous formalisation has been set up to monitor the huge volume of design documents generated by this contract.

All documents are identified uniquely in a computer system (TECDOC).

TECDOC is used to manage the issue status and movements of each document:-

- originator,
- state of development (revision index),
- status (for example, issued for construction),
- distribution (a vital stage in monitoring organisational interfaces).

Each document is examined closely by the manufacturers' team of engineers, then by that of TML, which systematically issues comment sheets (no approval by omission). This exchange continues until an approved document is obtained.

At the same time as this technical exchange, design meetings are regularly scheduled between TML and its subcontractors. Minutes are taken of each meeting and actions or agreements are clearly recorded.

4.2 Formal Design Review

In order to make sure that the development of the product design is not affected by major deviations, which could harm its overall performances (operational and safety performances), each contract is the subject of formal design reviews.

The latter are initially organised internally by each subcontractor.

Contracts were awarded on the basis of an outline design (APS). It is the responsibility of the subcontractors to draw up a detailed design (APD) and construction designs (PEO). TML mainly carries out formal design reviews with subcontractors at the end of the latter two phases.

These reviews consist of exhaustively evaluating the appropriate and coherent nature of the designs, both as regards the product itself and the internal and external interface implications for the rolling stock.

Bearing in mind the complexity of both the products, which are to a large extent new designs, and the organisations responsible, an operation of this kind involves the implementation of precise organisational procedures.

The latter are initiated and regularly assessed by TML Quality Assurance personnel. The goal is to ensure that the manufacturer is capable of presenting:-

- a precise management system for all technical documentation issued by the various engineering organisations,

- a full status report of variations, with their origins and their implication in the design document organisational structure,

- the status of these variations,

- an assessment of situations which are not finalised before the following development stage is begun.

At TML, the documentation used for formal design reviews is meticulously collated as follows:-

- comment sheets on design documents issued by manufacturers (routine checks),

- technical reports, minutes of interface meetings, etc.

This compiled data is analysed by a group of people whose responsibilities, specialised fields or professional experience cover all the areas involved in shuttle design: rolling stock, manufacturing technology, mechanics, electricity, electronics, computers, quality assurance, safety, operation. A summary report is drawn up following this analysis, and acts as a basis for the formal design review.

The latter consists of bringing together the work carried out by the four groups present (TML, Eurotunnel, the manufacturer and the MdO) in order to reveal any situation which might affect the final product, the construction programme, costs, procurement, manufacture, tests, etc..

A report identifying all the situations assessed and the recommended actions is used to monitor construction up to the final execution of the actions required.

Examples are appended of the "Action Sheet" (see Appendix 3A, 3B).

4.3 Prototype

Generally speaking, the design of the special solutions adopted for the construction of the project is validated by carrying out prototype tests on sub-assemblies.

A prototype programme goes through 4 phases:-

- definitions,
- development (manufacture of prototype),
- tests,
- analysis of results and return of information to definition phase (this analysis also constitutes a source of information to be used during formal design reviews).

This activity operates as a closed loop, until it is demonstrated that the product complies with contractual performance, safety, reliability and maintainability criteria.

This makes it possible, before starting industrial production:-

- to identify any design errors,
- to modify quality criteria of essential components, manufacturing tolerances, etc.
- to plan methods and procedures for industrial production.

This prototype phase has been used extensively to validate anti-fire protection measures.

Several model wagons, doors, windows and floors have been subject to fire tests. To validate the fire detection and extinguishing system, TML built a full scale model wagon, placed a coach on it and set fire to it at various points (engine, luggage compartment, seats, etc.)

Here again, TML Quality Assurance personnel play a significant role in both the definition and the operation of management systems for the prototypes, which must provide:-

- precise reference documents for each stage of development, including "retrofitting" of variations and adaptations, both for the prototype and for the industrial design of the product,

- reference documents kept permanently up to date, in the event of virtually inevitable variations during the manufacturing phase.

4.4 Type test

In accordance with UIC and IEC regulations, type tests are carried out to validate detailed designs.

All major pieces of equipment go through this phase: frames, bogies, brakes, ventilation, communications, electricity supply, traction.

The development and analysis phases are the same as for prototypes, with the important difference that the product tested is that which will be mass produced.

5 MANUFACTURING QA MONITORING

Quality Assurance during the manufacturing phase is based on a conventional quality management scheme as follows:-

- programming manufacturing and inspection operations (inspection and test plan),

- identifying means and methods (procedures and specifications for each operation),

- proof of execution (qualification reports, quality control certificates, test reports).

Two special measures reinforce these arrangements:-

- first article inspection,

- quality indicators.

5.1 F.A.I. (First Article Inspection)

Manufacturing methods and procedures are validated by setting up a special inspection and monitoring programme for the first article to come off the production line. The aim is to ensure that the required level of quality is achieved under mass production conditions, and to confirm that the configuration of the manufactured product corresponds to that of the designed and approved product.

F.A.I.s are conducted by the manufacturers on the suppliers' premises.

Depending on the nature of the equipment, an inspection team is formed by QA/QC, engineering and purchasing staff. The F.A.I. takes place in 3 stages:-

a. Preparation

Collation of information (drawings, documents, test reports, standards, etc.) for the concerned equipment.

b. Implementation

Inspection on the supplier's premises:-

- Performance tests,
- Physical characteristics (measurement readings),
- Functional tests,
- Non-destructive tests,
- Review of documentation,
- Packaging,
- Final visual inspection,
- Manufacturing methods,
- Identification,
- Management of configurations, prototypes, type tests, series.

A report is drawn up at the end of this phase.

c. Follow-up

Corrective actions identified during the F.A.I. are the subject of a follow-up until the problem is finally solved.

The manufacturing inspection and test plan for the concerned equipment is finalised at the end of this phase.

5.2 Manufacturing surveillance

The manufacturing inspection and test plan (list of manufacturing and inspection operations) is the basis for the quality surveillance carried out by TML.

Quality control is carried out by each manufacturer. TML checks that all the activities described in the manufacturing inspection and test plan are conducted according to the specified procedures, and that any discrepancy is recorded and corrected.

The surveillance is carried out by TML Resident Engineers in each factory where manufacturing takes place. In particular, they check that manufacturing conditions are satisfactory and they witness all the factory final inspections.

Factory Final Inspections are documented by the TML Resident Engineer by issuing the Quality Release Certificate (see example in Appendix 4) which is a necessary pre-condition for the dispatch of major equipment from one factory to another or completed wagons & Locos to the site.

5.3 Quality Indicators

The manufacturing quality level is monitored by setting up a Quality Indicator in each production shop. The parameter adopted (welding repair rate, dimensional examination, etc.) is analysed regularly and any negative variation in this parameter leads to corrective measures. See example Quality Indicator in Appendix 5.

5.4 Audits

Quality Assurance audits are regularly carried out to check that the suppliers' QA system is correctly implemented.

6 QUALITY OF COMMISSIONING

In addition to the equipment being well designed and well manufactured, it must be operational and safe.

A test programme for commissioning is specified, which allows all operational and safety functions to be systematically checked. Each test is the subject of a specification and a test report, which is analysed. Necessary modifications / retrofitting are immediately carried out and incorporated into all equipment. Starting with individual wagons, rolling stock will be gradually put together:-

- into three units: for example
  SDC (A) / SDC (S) / SDC (A)
  A standing for automatic coupler and S for semi-permanent coupler,

- into rakes: for example DDL + 4X (DDCA + DDCS + DDCA) + DDL (368 metres long),

- into trains: for example:-
  * **tourist train**: loco / SDC rake / DDC rake / loco (776 metres long),
  * **heavy goods train**: rear loco 2x (HGVL + 14 HGVC + HGVL) / amenity coach / front loco (727 metres long).

Systems (ventilation, control & communications, power supply) are thus integrated and tested progressively.

The final phase consists of running trains through the tunnel and checking the integration and interaction of rolling stock (shuttles) with fixed equipment (tunnel dynamic envelope, effect of PRD dampers, signalling, control and communications, etc.)

All this will allow a fast and completely safe journey between France and England:-

- 27 minutes in the tunnel,
- 35 minutes platform to platform journey (approximatively),
- 60 minutes between entering one Terminal and leaving the other Terminal.

APPENDICES

1. Channel Tunnel Organisation

2. Rolling Stock Manufacturers

3. Formal Design Review "Action Sheets" (Samples 3A, 3B)

4. Quality Release Certificate

5. Quality Indicator (sample).

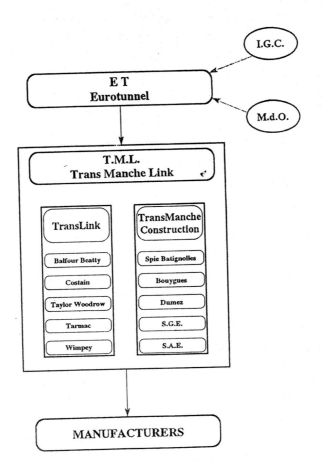

Channel Tunnel Organisations

Appendix 1

C451/018 © IMechE 1992

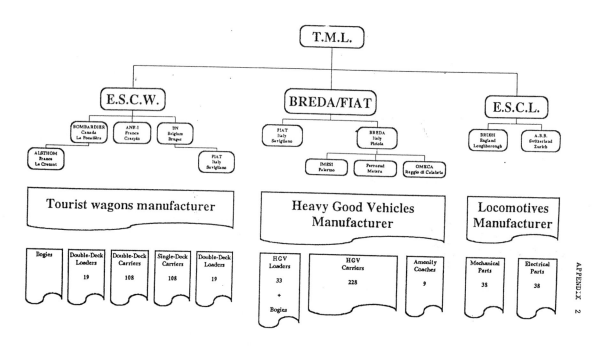

Rolling Stock Manufacturers

Appendix 2

FORMAL DESIGN REVIEW COMMITTEE

ACTION SHEET

Sheet 1 of 1

1.   This action sheet shall be completed when required by the Chairman following comments on the formal design review checklist (see Appendix "A").

2.   Complete the sheet and allot a registered number.

Review Checklist Item No.:	Registered No.: 2
Design Review Subject: Dwell Time	TOURIST WAGON

Summary of Comment from Comment Form - Identified Problem

Respect du temps d'ouverture discanopies
(AS N: 4 et 5 du precedent FDR)

Proposed Corrective Action   Verification du temps d'ouverture des canopies et de l'energie consommée pendant l'essai d'endurance en cours.

Signed
Review Engineer..   Date .3.1./.1.0./.9.1..

Formal Review Committe Action

Signed
Chairman.....................................   Date...31/10/91...

Sheet 1 of 1

1.   This action sheet shall be completed when required by the
        Chairman following comments on the formal design review
        checklist (see Appendix "A").

2.   Complete the sheet and allot a registered number.

Review Checklist Item No.:   Registered No.: 4
                                                TOURIST WAGON
Design Review Subject: *Evacuation*

Summary of Comment from Comment Form - Identified Problem

*Verification des espaces disponibles pour
l'evacuation.
(AS. N: 7 du precedent FDR)*

Proposed Corrective Action *Dessins donnant les espaces
libres intericurs tenant compte des tolerances.*

Signed
Review Engineer ....   Date 31/10/91

Formal Review Committe Action

Signed
Chairman ....   Date 31/10/91

APPENDIX 4

(TML) **ROLLING STOCK**
CONSTAT QUALITE - *QUALITY RELEASE*

No.	FIAT 92/001
	page 1 of 3

No. DE MARCHE *SUB-CONTRACT NUMBER* 123892	FOURNISSEUR *SUPPLIER* : FIAT FERROVIARIA
.. AMENDMENTS N. 6+12+17+18	SOUS-TRAITANT *SUB-SUPPLIER* :
DESIGNATION DU MARCHE *SUB-CONTRACT DESCRIPTION* LHGV WAGONS	ETABLISSEMENT *LOCATION* : SAVIGLIANO

Loco / Wagon / Vehicle or Equipment	Qté *Qty*	Documents décrivant la recette *Documents describing the equipment*	Identification des matériels *Equipment serial number*
LOADER COMPLETE WITH	1	CAR HISTORY BOOK:	WAGON N. 5801
BOGIES		Ref.C52 968 RBX BRED 9715 A	
		C52 968 RBX BRED 9716 A	
		QA DATA PACKAGE	
		Ref.C52 968 RBX BRED 9095 A	

Anomalies et réserves restant à lever *Non-conformances and reservations remaining to be resolved*	A lever *To be withdrawn*	
	Avant/*Before*	Par/*By*
Refer to herewith annexe 1 (pages 2 &3)		

OBSERVATIONS/COMMENTS

	L'INGENIEUR RESIDENT AQ/CQ DE TML *TML QA/QC RESIDENT ENGINEER*
	HOM *NAME* : R. HURIER
	FAIT A *DONE AT* : SAVIGLIANO LE *DATE* : 10/04/1992
	SIGNATURE *SIGNATURE* : R. HURIER

DISTRIBUTION: ORIGINAL TO SUPPLIER	ADDITIONAL DISTRIBUTION
COPIES TO 1 Quality Assurance (A.BONAERT 2 Project Manager (D.DARCY 3 Engineering (J.M. INGARDIN 4 Commercial Manager (R.BISHOP	B. PAVOT

Appendix 4

QUALITY INDICATOR
LHGV CARRIER.
WELDING REPAIR PERCENTAGE

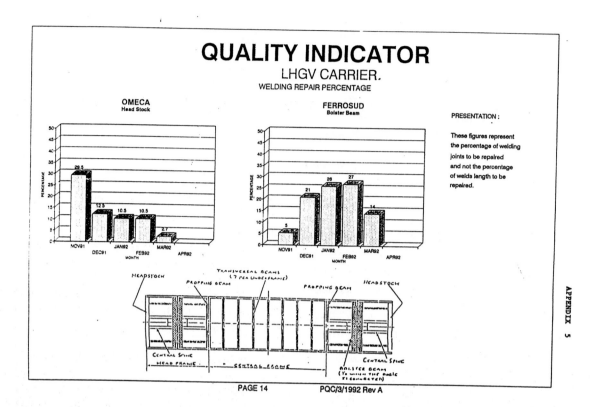

OMECA
Head Stock

FERROSUD
Bolster Beam

PRESENTATION :

These figures represent
the percentage of welding
joints to be repaired
and not the percentage
of welds length to be
repaired.

PAGE 14   PQC/3/1992 Rev A

The Channel Tunnel — commissioning the system

A PASCAL
Project Implementation Division, Eurotunnel, Folkestone, Kent

1 INTRODUCTION

1.1 Without going over in detail what the previous speakers have said, I think it is useful at the beginning of my presentation to point out a few important characteristics of the Channel Tunnel:

- The Channel Tunnel is a rail tunnel,

- a long rail tunnel,

- linking two European Community countries, the UK and France,

- which means creating a link not only between two territories but also between two cultures, two sets of traditions, two sets of regulations,

- Finally, it is a tunnel through which will travel not only Eurotunnel's own shuttles, but also main-line trains and freight trains chartered by the National Railways of the surrounding countries (British Rail, the SNCF, and less directly the SNCB).

1.2 The originality of the commissioning and start-up programme which is going to be presented to you is largely the product of the above characteristics. This includes:

- series of tests intended to demonstrate the availability and safety of the system;

- series of tests intended to satisfy the various parties involved, both directly (companies involved in the operation of the tunnel), and indirectly (supervisory bodies).

1.3 After this introduction I am now going to go over the following points:

- the general organisation of the tests,

- staff training and clarification of regulations and usage procedures.

- the role of the various parties involved,
- and start up of operations proper.

These points will of course be presented with the idea of illustrating method without claiming to be exhaustive.

2 GENERAL ORGANISATION OF TESTS

2.1 The commissioning and start up programme essentially comprises three kinds of tests:

- Tests to check the conformity of various equipment to the plans (supply, rolling stock, signalling). These are the equipment acceptance test.

- Global tests concerning the operation of the system under normal conditions and under certain standard downgraded conditions (eg trains backing up at a point in the tunnel); these are tests on completion.

- investigative tests, theoretically not structure related, but intended to gather information on very specific configurations (eg total cut of one of the two main sub-stations).

2.2 The equipment acceptance tests are organised in a linear fashion, according to the theoretical diagram shown in figure 1.

In other words, the system is divided into a number of basic sub-systems (ventilation, pumping, rolling stock, tolls,...). Each sub-system is divided into test batches (a pumping station, a train, an electricity sub-station,...). Procedures are applied to these batches.

2.3 To give a breakdown by size, there are:

- 50 main sub-systems
- 500 tests batches
- 5000 procedures.

4 The process is going to involve a step-by-step test of the logic peculiar to each system and its interfaces with the upstream and lateral systems (CF figure 1). Of note in this process is the special role played by the Control Centre equipment: RTM or train management system; EMS or electromechanical equipment management.

5 The tests on completion are organised in two stages (CF figure 2):

- An initial phase intended to eliminate all train traffic prohibition. This will include:

  . checking the railway gauge,
  . checking the track and catenary,
  . checking the aerodynamic tests,
  . checking the signalling (track-side equipment and on-train equipment),
  . measuring the stopping distances of the speed control system,
  . checking shuttle protection against the effects of wind in the terminals.

- At the end of the initial stage, trains which have been tested can travel through the tunnel with no limitations other than standard regulation limitations. This initial stage is concluded by an observation period during which the idea is to have two trains running at the minimum interval planned at opening, ie three minutes. Tests will be carried out to determine the absolute minimum interval.

- A second phase intended to ensure the system's performance under the most likely operational conditions: this stage will include such tests as:

  . train movement quality

  . the aerodynamic effects inside trains (pressure variations, ...)

  . standard travel time of various trains

  . the operational possibilities under downgraded conditions (train recovery, signalling box breakdown, Control Centre breakdown)

  . behaviour of the system when fully loaded

. measurement of the toll system rate of flow,...

- This second stage will end with a 15 day trial period involving operating the system eight hours a day according to the timetables planned at start up.

2.6 Let us now give a few examples of tests quite specific to the Channel Tunnel:

1st example: aerodynamic tests

- The aerodynamic tests form part of the initial stage of the tests on completion;

- the aim is to check that air movements in the same tunnel, or between tunnels via the piston-relief ducts, are not likely to have unacceptable effects:

  . in terms of pressure and air speed,
  . when manoeuvring the various doors in the system (cross-passage doors, crossover doors, wagon end doors),
  . on trains and their loads, particularly regarding HGV's transported by shuttle or freight wagons,
  . on the comfort of passengers and personnel,
  . on the behaviour of the trains' pantograph.

- Figures 3, 4 and 5 respectively show:

  . a standard test configuration
  . tunnel instrumentation at a piston-relief duct in the text zone
  . the instrumentation of a test train

2nd example: evacuation tests

- The evacuation tests form part of the second stage of tests on completion.

- Their objective is to check the application of evacuation principles in the planned tunnel operation configurations, using a set of basic tests.

- The method used is to identify all the safety actions necessary to manage evacuation and to individually test these actions in their worst case.

- This results in four basic test categories:

  . Category 1: Tests in the tunnel with passengers (essentially evacuation movements inside a train or from a train to the service tunnel);

. Category 2: Tests with passengers carried out on emergency track instead of the tunnel; essentially supplementary to the preceding tests;

. Category 3: Tests not requiring passengers (activation of the first emergency level, implementation of the standard response, reconfiguration of signalling);

. Category 4: Miscellaneous tests (train movements at varying speeds, stopping and restarting of trains, operation of the various tunnel doors);

- The process is completed by a full-scale evacuation exercise using 7 trains and a few hundred people, 15 of whom will act as handicapped passengers.

3 STAFF TRAINING: CLARIFICATION OF REGULATIONS AND VARIOUS USAGE PROCEDURES

3.1 The system test period is the privileged opportunity to check consistency between 3 principal elements:

- equipment
- personnel taken to be qualified responsible for operating the equipment
- equipment usage methods for either operation or maintenance. This is why we think it is useful to give some information on these points.

3.2 **The regulations and procedures first of all**:

The general tunnel operation regulations comprise 6 volumes on the following subjects:

Volume A: General points on Eurotunnel
Volume B: General description of the system
Volume C: Railway operation
Volume D: Road operation
Volume E: Treatment and coordination of a major incident
Volume F: Transport of dangerous goods

The general documents are approved by the authority in charge of supervision.

Supporting these general regulations are instructions (about 1800) presented on an organisation chart similar to the one in figure 6.

All these instructions must of course be checked during actual operation.

3.3 **Staff training now**:

To give some idea of the scale of the problem regarding Eurotunnel staff alone:

- 2000 officials to train
- 8000 man/months of training
- 70 "classrooms"
- about 130 different classes

This training mainly involves:

- general training elements, particularly language training. It has been decided that, given their role, Eurotunnel officials should have a relatively thorough knowledge of English and French.

- Training in general regulations and procedures.

- Specific training on the various equipment.

- This training can take the following form:

. theoretical lessons in classes (lectures or computer-assisted teaching)

. or training using simulators (eg driving simulator)

. or practical training on site. To this end, during the tests on completion, a little less than one third of the tunnel usage time will be used for training.

This training will be given:

. by the ancillary staff of the contractor, TML, or of its sub-contractors,

. or by Eurotunnel personnel.

4 THE ROLE OF THE VARIOUS PARTIES INVOLVED

4.1 **The role of the contractor Transmanche Link**

Apart from its obvious contribution of constructing the project, TML is responsible for organising and carrying out the tests. To this end, it is responsible for the following:

- drawing up the various test procedures (I remind you that it is planned to have 5000 of these),

- supplying and setting up the instrumentation required for the various tests,

- scheduling and managing the implementation of the various tests,

- writing the test reports,

- and of course at the end of it all, rectifying any anomalies indicated by the tests.

At the height of the tests, the number of TML officials responsible just for organising and managing the tests will reach 150 people. This figure does not include all those directly involved in operation (drivers, supervisors, operators,...).

4.2   Eurotunnel's role

Apart from its primary role of client, who is responsible for checking the quality of what is being supplied to it, Eurotunnel is responsible for providing the personnel required for operational and maintenance activities during the test period.

Rather than just provide TML with a mass of people, leaving their management and activity scheduling up to TML, Eurotunnel has preferred to retain a stronger control of its officials and therefore is more involved, in terms of organisation, in this task.

This orientation demonstrates Eurotunnel's firm wish to take advantage of the tests to finalise the organisational and management methods which will be used on opening.
Figure 7 shows the outline of what the distribution of roles could be during the commissioning phase. This document is only given as an indication as at the time of writing this paper, it was still being discussed with TML.

4.3   The role of the Intergovernmental Commission and the Safety Authority

The Intergovernmental Commission, which has 14 members (7 British, 7 French) has a double role: it must first of all check that everything constructed and its planned use is in accordance with the Concession agreement; it must then, and this is not its lesser role, "facilitate the

completion of the work", ie it is its job to come up with compromises when there are apparent incompatibilities between the legislation, procedures or traditions of the two countries. The allocation of radio frequencies is quite a good example of this: it can be said, without drawing too much of a caricature, that the frequencies reserved in France for civil use are reserved in the UK for military use and vice versa.

It is assisted in its role by a Safety Authority with 10 members (5 British, 5 French) which is more directly responsible for all safety aspects: railway safety, work safety, civil safety.

Beyond the examination of the 'avant-projets' (outline and definite designs) and the construction standards, the Intergovernmental Commission, like the Safety Authority, is responsible for checking that what is carried out is in accordance with the approved documents; to a large extent, this involves checking that the proposed test programmes are sufficient to be convincing. The Safety Authority has a representative on each site who is responsible for supervising commissioning operations.

4.4   The role of the 'Maitre d'Oeuvre'

The 'Maitre d'Oeuvre' notion is provided for by the concession, but its role is completely different from the one normally given in France to the 'Maitre d'Oeuvre'. In fact, the 'Maitre d'Oeuvre' is the assistant of the Commission responsible for permanently supervising the proper progress of operations.

Its role regarding commissioning is therefore fundamental, as it has to report to the Commission on the results of the tests.

4.5   The role of the National Railways

The intervention of the National Railways, BR and the SNCF, is limited to the commissioning operations and checking the appropriateness of the rolling stock they propose for use in the tunnel system. The main points to be checked, which are specific to the tunnel, are essentially the aerodynamic effects on the pantographs or on the wagons at the piston-relief ducts between tunnels. Other points to be checked are much more standard (movement quality, tapping of the current, signalling,...).

START UP

.1 As provided for in the various contractual documents, start up of the system is presented as an entity, including:

- Eurotunnel passenger shuttles,
- Eurotunnel HGV shuttle,
- the national railways' high-speed trains,
- the national railways' freight trains.

.2 In fact, as is always the case in projects of this size, grains of sand suddenly appear, which slow down the operation of some gearing or other or even damage it. I think that you are more or less aware of the difficulties encountered. Today I would only like to deal with one of them, that is the delay in rolling stock delivery.

In fact, instead of the various rolling stock items being implemented at the same time, there is likely to be staggered implementation over a period of time:

- the HGV shuttles would be the first to come out, followed by the passenger shuttles. The high-speed trains and the freight train locomotives would be delayed by several months in relation to the preceding ones.

This situation naturally has an effect on commissioning: for example, there will be changes in the way in which the aerodynamic tests or the fully-loaded supply tests are carried out. Another example, some tests will have to be postponed until the rolling stock is available, in certain cases that being after the initial start up.

But these delays are going to above all affect start up itself, which in fact will only be able to be progressive:

- first of all, HGV transport service
- simultaneous launch of an inaugural car and coach transport service
- a few months later, moving on to the definitive passenger shuttle service and launch of the high-speed train service, perhaps initially in the form of an inaugural service.

The problem of launching the freight train service is still being examined. As it only involves traction units BR and the SNCF are examining the possibility of using existing locomotives which would be adapted as required.

6 CONCLUSIONS

What conclusions can be drawn from all this?

- The first conclusion is that, just because of its special nature, the Channel Tunnel is going to give rise to a considerably larger commissioning programme than that required by a traditional railway line. The main points of this programme have been decided; the implementation documents are almost all written; there are still some doubts regarding carrying out the tests, given the delays in delivery of the rolling stock or of certain equipment...

- The future operators of the system have started recruitment and training and they will be almost ready at the end of this year, which was the date initially planned for the tests on completion to start.

- The operational regulations and various instructions have been written and are being finalised.

- The future operators are currently feeling a little betrayed by the contractors, who are not managing to complete the project as quickly as planned. They are obliged to wait, ready to act when the time comes. They also have to stagger the start up of the tunnel.

- Regrettable as they are, all these things are part of the realities of life.

- But I believe that beyond the present economic difficulties, thanks to the extreme goodwill of all the staff of the Operating company, the operation of the tunnel will quickly be a success, the main beneficiaries of which will be our clients.

C451/025 © IMechE 1992

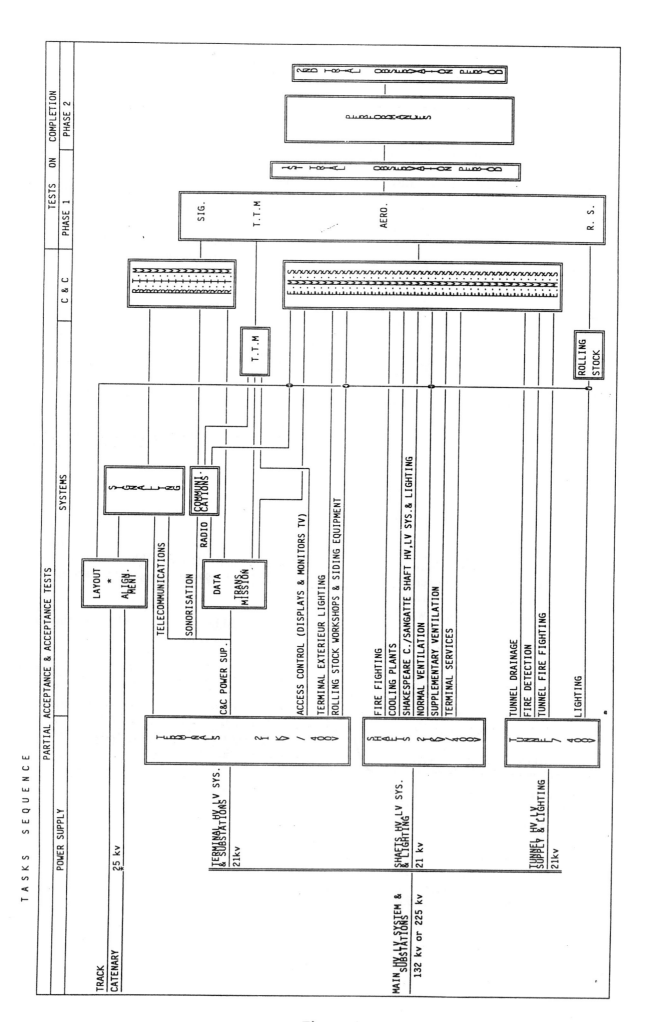

Figure 1

TESTS ON COMPLETION LOGIC

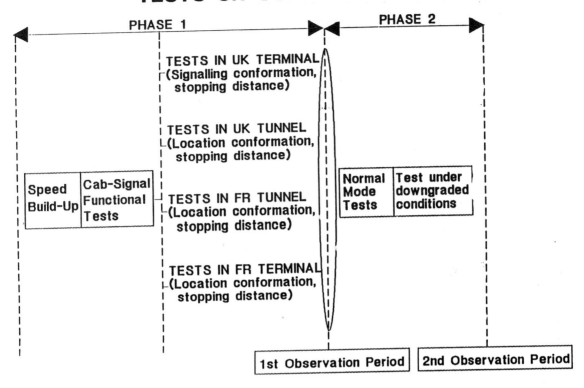

Figure 2

Aerodynamics Commissioning
Example Test Configuration

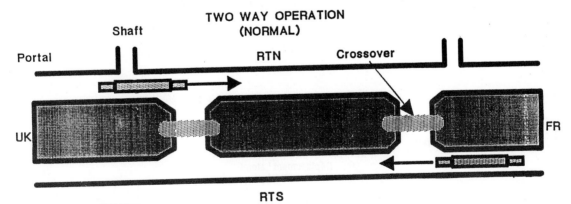

TEST SEQUENCE

One off TSh and one off HGV carry out three
round trips, crossing near mid-point.
UK entry seven minutes ahead of FR entry.
Shuttles to be reversed such that leading
locomotive becomes trailing locomotive.

Figure 3

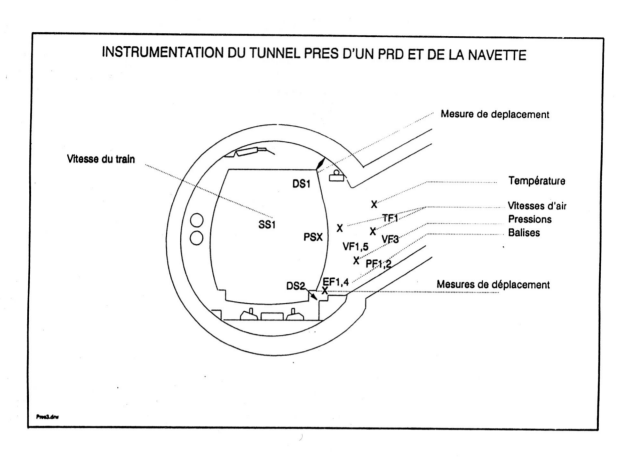

Figure 4

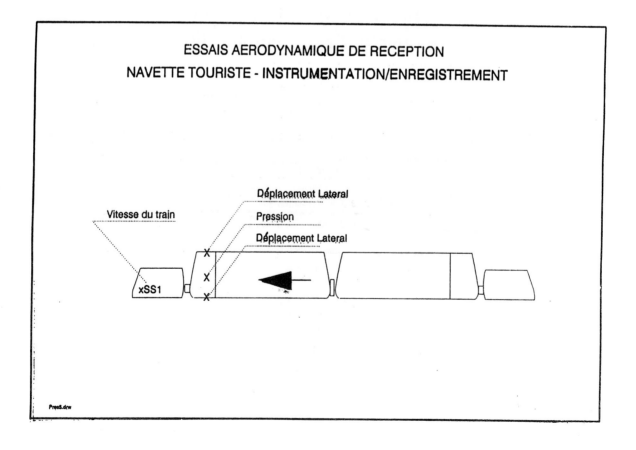

Figure 5

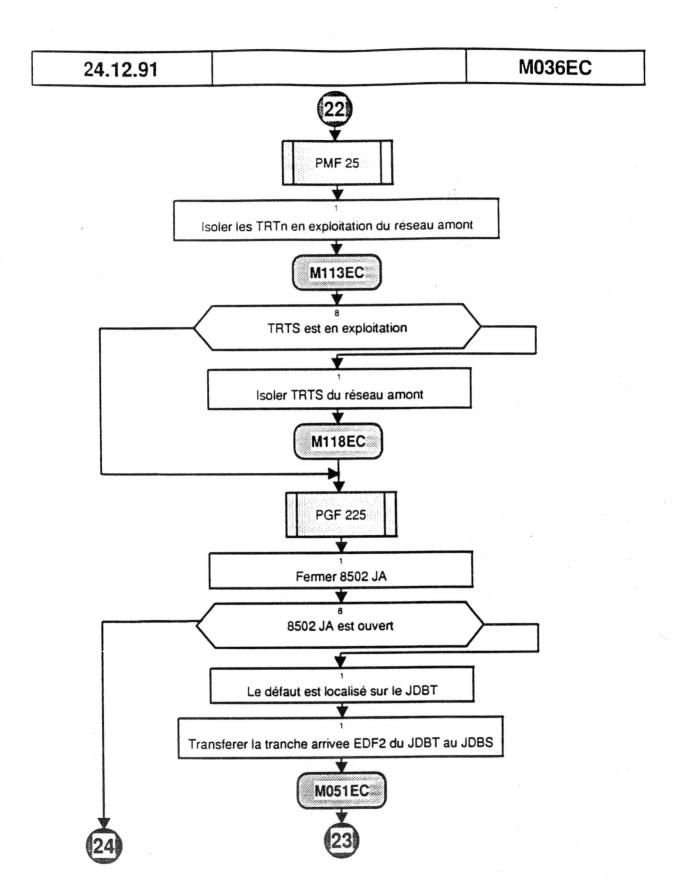

Figure 6

INDICATIVE RESPECTIVE INVOLVEMENT

OF ET AND TML DURING TESTS ON COMPLETION

	Diesel locos circulation	Electric locos tests	RCC fully commiss. RTM + EMS	Tests on completion	"Marche à blanc"
Drivers	ET	ET	ET	ET	ET
Drivers management.	ET	ET	ET	ET	ET
Operational instructions in a tests programme frame	TML	TML	TML	TML	ET
RCC controllers management	–	–	ET	ET	ET
Power supply centralised control (24h/24)...	–	–	ET	ET	ET
Substations local operation (normal or incidents)..........	TML	TML	TML	TML	ET
Operational coordination transport, "consignations".....	TML	TML	TML	TML	ET

Figure 7